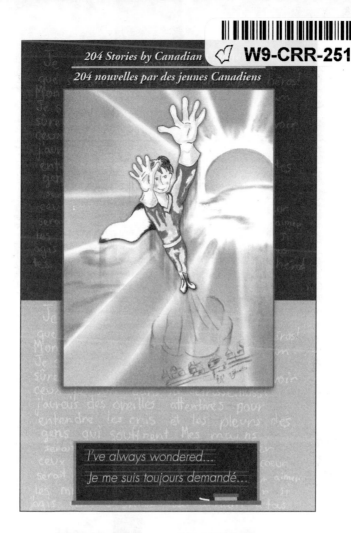

204 Stories by Canadian

204 nouvelles par des jeunes Canadiens

W9-CRR-251

I've always wondered...

Je me suis toujours demandé...

Published by/Publié par

The Business Depot Ltd.
30 Centurian Drive, Suite 106
Markham, Ontario, L3R 8B9

Find us on the World Wide Web at: staples.ca or bureauengros.com
Nous nous trouvons sur le Web à : bureauengros.com ou staples.ca

Copyright ©2005
The Business Depot Ltd.

STAPLES Business Depot/ Bureau en gros will donate all net proceeds from book sales for even distribution among over 200 of the Canadian schools with students submitting entries, selected by draw. Additionally, STAPLES Business Depot/Bureau en gros will donate gift cards that will be presented to the school of our First-Prize winner.

STAPLES Business Depot/ Bureau en gros fera don de toutes les recettes nettes provenant des ventes de ce livre en les distribuant équitablement entre plus de 200 écoles des étudiants participants, choisies par tirage. De plus, STAPLES Business Depot/ Bureau en gros fera don de cartes-cadeaux qui seront offertes à l'école du gagnant du premier prix.

For further details of donations contributed to schools by STAPLES Business Depot/Bureau en gros, please write to:

Pour de plus amples détails concernant les dons faits aux écoles par STAPLES Business Depot/Bureau en gros, veuillez écrire à :

P.O. Box 3619 Industrial Park, Markham, ON, L3R 9Z9

Book and cover design/conception du livre et de la couverture : Isabelle Tremblay
Cover illustration/illustration de la couverture : Tiziana Guido
First imprint/première date de publication: March/mars 2005
ISBN 0-9689688-4-8
Printed and bound in Canada   Imprimé et relié au Canada

Acknowledgements

STAPLES Business Depot/Bureau en gros would like to thank the following organizations and individuals for their efforts in making this book possible:

- Paulette Bourgeois
- Tiziana Guido for her illustration
- HP Compaq for their generous prize donations of a computer and a digital camera.
- Solisco Printers Toronto for their printing contributions.
- The thousands of children from across Canada who entered the challenge. Without their submissions, we would not have been able to compile such an outstanding anthology of stories.
- All the STAPLES Business Depot/Bureau en gros associates who supported this project by donating their time and individual talents in the many different aspects in the creation of this book.

And... a big Thank You to all of you who have contributed toward the education of Canadian children by purchasing this book!

Remerciements

STAPLES Business Depot/Bureau en gros aimerait remercier les organisations et personnes suivantes pour les efforts fournis pour réaliser ce livre :

- Paulette Bourgeois
- Tiziana Guido pour son illustration
- HP Compaq pour leur don généreux d'un ordinateur et d'un appareil photo numérique.
- Solisco Printers Toronto pour sa contribution à l'impression de ce livre.
- Les milliers d'enfants dans tout le Canada qui ont participé au concours. Sans eux, nous ne pourrions compiler cette extraordinaire anthologie de nouvelles.
- Tous les associés de STAPLES Business Depot/Bureau en gros qui ont aidé à ce projet en donnant leur temps et leurs talents individuels dans les nombreux aspects de la création de ce livre.

Et... un grand merci à vous tous qui avez contribué à l'éducation des enfants canadiens en achetant ce livre !

Foreword by

Steve Matyas,
President,
STAPLES Business Depot/
Bureau en gros

It is my pleasure to welcome you to our fourth annual national writing challenge for children.

I'm reminded of the adage that in choosing to take even the smallest of actions, each and every one of us has the power to influence the state of this world and make it a better place. In 2001, we chose to champion the value of literacy by providing a forum for our young people to unleash their imaginations, have fun writing creatively, and gain rewards for their efforts. The results far surpassed our expectations. Not only were a huge number of young people inspired to write and submit stories, but, as well, there was plenty of evidence to prove that Canada will be enjoying a whole new crop of award-winning authors in the future!

In a nutshell, every ounce of encouragement provided today could make all the difference to a child's tomorrow. Congratulations to all the young people who submitted stories. Keep writing, give your imagination free rein, and feed your dreams.

Thank you,

4

J'ai le plaisir de vous accueillir à notre quatrième concours d'écriture annuel à l'échelle nationale destiné aux enfants.

Je me rappelle de l'adage selon lequel toute action, même petite, donne à chacun de nous le pouvoir d'influencer le monde et de le rendre meilleur. En 2001, nous avons choisi de patronner l'alphabétisme en offrant à nos jeunes une tribune pour donner libre cours à leur imagination, pour qu'ils s'amusent en écrivant d'une façon créative et pour les récompenser de leurs efforts. Les résultats ont de loin dépassé nos attentes. Non seulement un grand nombre de jeunes ont été inspirés pour écrire et envoyer leur histoire, mais nous pouvons aussi prouver avec certitude que le Canada jouira, à l'avenir, d'une nouvelle génération de jeunes auteurs primés !

En un mot, chaque brin d'encouragement offert aujourd'hui pourrait faire toute la différence dans la vie d'un enfant. Félicitations à tous les jeunes qui ont envoyé leur histoire. Continuez à écrire, ne freinez pas votre imagination et nourrissez vos rêves.

Merci.

S Matyas

Préface par

Steve Matyas,
Président,
STAPLES Business Depot/
Bureau en gros

Foreword by

Paulette Bourgeois,
Children's Book Author

I've never written such a short, short story in my entire life, and it wasn't an easy assignment. I thought it would be simple to find 100 words that flowed together to make a story, but I was just getting rolling on my character, and my plot, when I realized that I had already written 500 words. I hadn't even thought of a good ending, yet! It took a long time, and a dozen crumpled attempts before this little story seemed just right. But I learned something important in the process: each word counts.

Imagine how powerful a toddler feels when he or she first uses the word, "No!" A writer, too, starts to realize that he or she can make a good story great just by choosing the right word for the right place. Long ago a teacher told me to think about each of the five senses when I wrote. So whenever I write a description I ask myself if there is anything special about the way a thing or a place looks, tastes, smells, feels or sounds. A basement is just a basement until you tell the reader that the walls are dripping green slime and it stinks like the bottom of a hamster's cage. The best stories use rich, meaningful language that jumps off the page. A character could walk, but he might as easily, stumble, pace, plod, lurch, waddle or stride.

I admire all of the students who embraced the challenge to write a story in a hundred words and I congratulate the writers whose work appears in this book. They certainly made every word count.

Je n'ai jamais écrit une nouvelle si courte et cela n'a pas été une tâche facile. J'ai pensé qu'il serait facile de trouver 100 mots qui se lieraient pour faire une histoire. À peine ai-je commencé à créer mon personnage et l'histoire que je me suis rendu compte que j'avais déjà écrit 500 mots, et je n'avais même pas pensé à une bonne fin. Après un certain temps et plusieurs tentatives, cette petite nouvelle fut enfin prête. J'ai appris une chose importante durant le processus : chaque mot compte.

Imaginez le pouvoir qu'un enfant semble posséder lorsqu'il utilise le mot « Non ! » pour la première fois. De même, un écrivain commence à se rendre compte qu'il peut écrire une excellente histoire rien qu'en choisissant le bon mot pour l'utiliser au bon endroit. Il y a longtemps, un enseignant m'avait dit de penser à chacun des cinq sens en écrivant. Alors, chaque fois que je décris une chose ou un endroit, je me demande s'il y a quelque chose de particulier concernant la vue, le goût, l'odorat, le toucher ou l'ouïe. Un sous-sol est rien qu'un sous-sol jusqu'à ce que vous révéliez au lecteur que les murs sont gluants de substance verte et qu'il sent comme le fond de la cage d'un hamster. Les meilleures histoires utilisent un langage riche et intelligent qui ressort sur chaque page. Un personnage peut marcher mais il peut aussi bien trébucher, arpenter, cheminer, tituber ou se dandiner.

J'admire tous les élèves qui ont relevé le défi d'écrire une nouvelle de cent mots et je félicite les écrivains dont l'œuvre est publiée dans ce livre. Ils ont certainement donné de l'importance à chaque mot.

Préface par

Paulette Bourgeois,
auteure de livres d'enfants

Paulette Bourgeois

Paulette Bourgeois was never sure what she wanted to be when she grew up. She worked in an ice-cream parlour and sold flowers before she went to university to study Occupational Therapy. After working in a hospital she returned to school and studied journalism. It was only after her daughter was born in 1983 that Paulette decided to write children's books. One night she was watching a rerun of the television show, M*A*S*H* where the main character, Hawkeye Pierce, said he was so claustrophobic that if he were a turtle he would be afraid of his own shell. The next day, Paulette wrote Franklin in the Dark. Six publishers rejected the story, but Kids Can Press published the book in 1986, just after Paulette's son was born. Since then, the author has written science books including, The Sun and The Moon, and many picture books including, the award-winning Oma's Quilt. The Franklin stories have sold millions of copies around the world.

Now that Paulette's children are away at university, she spends her time writing magazine articles, studying French, travelling, and rewriting a novel that doesn't yet seem to have the right words in the right places.

I've always wondered how my dog Fred, a cocker spaniel with sad brown eyes, found out that he is ranked last on a list of the top twenty intelligent dog breeds. I suspect Fifi told him. She's the poodle next door. French poodles are the second smartest dogs in the world. So now, instead of chasing squirrels, Fred pretends to be a smart, French dog. He wears a beret and he comes when I call, "Ici, garcon!" I loved the old, dumb Fred, but there are advantages to a dog who wants to improve himself. Fred no longer eats my homework… he does it!

Paulette Bourgeois

Paulette Bourgeois n'a jamais su ce qu'elle voulait devenir lorsqu'elle serait grande. Elle a travaillé dans un café glacier et a vendu des fleurs avant d'aller à l'université pour étudier l'ergothérapie. Après avoir travaillé dans un hôpital, elle est retournée à l'école pour étudier le journalisme. C'est seulement après la naissance de sa fille en 1983 que Paulette a décidé d'écrire des livres pour enfants. Un soir, elle regardait M*A*S*H*, série retélévisée, dans lequel le personnage principal, Hawkeye Pierce, disait être si claustrophobique que s'il était une tortue, il aurait peur de sa propre coquille. Le lendemain, Paulette écrit <u>Franklin in the Dark</u> (<u>Benjamin et la nuit</u>). Six éditeurs rejettent l'histoire, mais la maison d'édition Kids Can Press la publie en 1986, juste après la naissance de son fils. Depuis, l'auteure a écrit des livres scientifiques comme <u>The Sun</u> et <u>The Moon</u> et plusieurs livres illustrés, y compris, le livre primé <u>Oma's Quilt</u>. Les histoires de Benjamin se sont vendues par millions dans le monde entier.

Maintenant que les enfants de Paulette sont à l'université, elle passe son temps à écrire des articles pour revues, à étudier le français, à voyager et à réécrire un roman où les bons mots n'ont pas trouvé encore leur juste place.

Paulette Bourgeois

Je me suis toujours demandé comment Fred, mon cocker spaniel aux yeux bruns tristes, a découvert qu'il était le dernier des vingt chiens les plus intelligents. Je suspecte Fifi, le caniche d'à côté, de le lui avoir dit. Les caniches français sont classés deuxièmes sur la liste des chiens les plus intelligents. Alors, maintenant, au lieu de chasser les écureuils, Fred se prend pour un chien français, porte un béret et vient lorsque je lui dis « Ici, garçon ! » J'aimais mon vieux nigaud de Fred, mais en s'améliorant, Fred ne mange plus mes devoirs… Il les fait !

Paulette Bourgeois

1

FIRST PLACE
PREMIÈRE PLACE

Samuel Turcotte

10 ans, St-Hyacinthe, QC
École Douville

Illustrated by/Illustration par Tiziana Guido

Je me suis toujours demandé ce que ce serait si j'étais un super héros! Mon prénom pourrait être Super-Sam. Je serais grand et gentil. J'aurais sûrement des yeux de lynx pour voir ceux qui sont dans la détresse. Aussi j'aurais des oreilles attentives pour entendre les cris et les pleurs des gens qui souffrent. Mes mains serait assez grandes pour relever ceux qui sont tombés. Et Mon coeur serait énorme comme la lune pour aimer les malheureux. Mais à bien y penser si j'agis comme un bon samaritain à tous les jours, je suis donc un sper héros!

Samuel Turcotte 10 ans

Je me suis toujours demandé ce que ce serait si j'étais un super héros ! Mon prénom pourrait être Super-Sam. Je serais grand et gentil. J'aurais sûrement des yeux de lynx pour voir ceux qui sont dans la détresse. Aussi j'aurais des oreilles attentives pour entendre les cris et les pleurs des gens qui souffrent. Mes mains seraient assez grandes pour relever ceux qui sont tombés. Et mon coeur serait énorme comme la lune pour aimer les malheureux. Mais à bien y penser si j'agis comme un bon samaritain à tous les jours, je suis donc un super héros !

For the English translation, please see page 215.

Samuel Turcotte, 10 ans, St-Hyacinthe, QC
École Douville

I've always wondered what it would be like to be a great hockey player. I could flip a wrist shot through the air like a flying bullet. Goalies would fear my shot. The fans would roar when I step on the ice. The coach calls my name "Graeme! We need a goal to tie the game." As quick as lightning I skate up the ice. With two seconds left I see a small gap in the net. I flip the puck. It flies past the goalie. The fans roar as the buzzer rings. "Brring." My mom calls, "Graeme wake up."

SECOND PLACE/DEUXIÈME PLACE

Graeme Kendall, Age 8, Calgary, AB
École Elbow Valley Elementary

Je me suis toujours demandé où vont les chaussettes qui disparaissent dans les sécheuses. Mon tiroir est rempli de chaussettes dépareillées. Mais où vont ces chaussettes perdues? Moi, je pense qu'elles sont aspirées dans le tuyau de la sécheuse et qu'elles sortent une à une, attirées vers une planète inconnue. Sur cette planète vivent des extra-terrestres qui ont froid aux pieds et qui les attirent avec leurs antennes. Je crois que notre seule chance de retrouver nos chaussettes c'est si leur planète se réchauffe et qu'ils décident de les retourner. J'imagine la pluie de chaussettes qui nous tombera du ciel!

Noêmie Robitaille   11 ans

Je me suis toujours demandé où vont les chaussettes qui disparaissent dans les sécheuses. Mon tiroir est rempli de chaussettes dépareillées. Mais où vont ces chaussettes perdues ? Moi, je pense qu'elles sont aspirées dans le tuyau de la sécheuse et qu'elles sortent une à une, attirées vers une planète inconnue. Sur cette planète vivent des extraterrestres qui ont froid aux pieds et qui les attirent avec leurs antennes. Je crois que notre seule chance de retrouver nos chaussettes c'est si leur planète se réchauffe et qu'ils décident de les retourner. J'imagine la pluie de chaussettes qui nous tombera du ciel !

THIRD PLACE/TROISIÈME PLACE

Noémie Robitaille, 11 ans, Hull, QC
École du Mont-Bleu

I've always wondered what it would be like to own a Pegasus. To be able to go anywhere in the world in a matter of hours I could go see the ancient castles of Britain, or the Parthenon in Greece. Maybe I'd like to go to Everest and visit the Khumbu Icefall or Hillary's Steps. Or maybe to Africa to visit the various indigenous peoples there and gaze at the tallest mountain on it's continent. I might even have some fun with the human mind and startle some airline passengers with my appearance at the window beside their seat.

Gabriel Levente Pandy-Szekeres, 12

I've always wondered what it would be like to own a Pegasus.
To be able to go anywhere in the world in a matter of hours.
I could go see the ancient castles of Britain or the Parthenon in
Greece. Maybe I'd like to go to Everest and visit Khumbu icefall
or Hillary's Steps, or maybe to Africa to visit the various
indigenous peoples there and gaze at the tallest mountain on its
continent. I might even have some fun with the human mind and
startle some airline passengers with my appearance at the
window beside their seat.

Honourable Mention/Mention honorable

Gabriel Levente Pandy-Szekeres, Age 12, Caledon, ON
Caledon East P.S.

I've always wondered why parents always say they were sooo perfect as kids when they weren't. I dug up some information by asking my grandma and trust me, parents weren't perfect! When my mom was young she knocked down her dresser by climbing on the drawers. Her parents didn't want it to happen again so they nailed her dresser to the floor! Can you belive that? Also one day my mom went to school only in her slip because she forgot to put on her skirt! If you want to learn about your parents, talk to your grandparents right now!

Michelle Abbott Age: 10

I've always wondered why parents always say they were sooo perfect as kids when they weren't. I dug up some information by asking my grandma and trust me, parents weren't perfect! When my mom was young she knocked down her dresser by climbing on the drawers. Her parents didn't want it to happen again so they nailed her dresser to the floor! Can you believe that? Also one day my mom went to school only in her slip because she forgot to put on her skirt! If you want to learn about your parents, talk to your grandparents right now!

Michelle Abbott, Age 10, Scarborough, ON
William G. Davis

15

Je me suis toujours demandé comment la parole est apparue.
Un jour un géant faisait des gros grognements. Ils ressemblaient
à des mots. Personne ne l'aimait parce qu'il faisait mal aux
oreilles. Alors le Dieu des communications est apparu. Il a
rapetissé le géant à la taille de l'homme. Ses grognements
sonnaient comme une flûte. Il s'est rapproché de tous les autres
pour leur dire « Bonjour ». Le son de sa voix était si magnifique
qu'ils voulurent tous devenir pareil. Alors le Dieu des
communications les a tous transformé. La parole était apparue.

Guillaume Allain, 10 ans, Sept-Iles, QC
École Gamache

I've always wondered why they built the Great Wall of China? Could it be because people wanted to stay in or to stay out?

The People must have been very sad. I would be if I could not see my family or friends.

It seems silly to me to have a big wall that all kids could not play together.

I think that everyone should always be friends and get along.

There are too many wars. That is sad.

No walls of any kind should be built anymore.

We should all learn to get along and be friends.

A world of Peace Forever.

Abigayle Alterton Age 10

I've always wondered why they built the Great Wall of China? Could it be because people wanted to stay in or to stay out? The people must have been very sad. I would be if I could not see my family or friends. It seems silly to me to have a big wall that all kids could not play together. I think that everyone should be friends and get along. There are too many wars. That is sad. No walls of any kind should be built anymore. We should all learn to get along and be friends. A world of peace, forever.

Abigayle Alterton, Age 10, Fredericton, AB
Garden Creek

I've always wondered what was spoken before language was developed. When children learn how to communicate, it sounds like meaningless mumbling. However, it is the child's attempt to echo the sounds they hear spoken around them. Then we must ask ourselves, how did the first people speak as children if they had no words to mimick? In documentaries "cavemen" were scruffy, unkept beings who communicated through grunts. I believe the first language developed, eventually evolved from those grunts. Although, there is no proof to support this theory. Personally, this interesting topic is a mystery that will always keep me guessing.

Rosemary Altobelli, 12

I've always wondered what was spoken before language was developed. When children learn how to communicate, it sounds like meaningless mumbling. However, it is the child's attempt to echo the sounds they hear spoken around them. Then we must ask ourselves, how did the first people speak as children if they had no words to mimick? In documentaries "cavemen" were scruffy, unkept beings who communicated through grunts. I believe the first language developed eventually evolved from those grunts. Although, there is no proof to support this theory. Personally, this interesting topic is a mystery that will always keep me guessing.

Rosemary Altobelli, Age 12, Woodbridge, On
St Francis de Sales

I've always wondered why
the snitzelbopper that lives
under my bed licks my toes
at night, I caught him once
and gave him quite a fright.
He jumped, hopped meowed, barked
and scurried under my bed, at
that point, I was sure I should
call him Ned. "Friend, friend, friend,"
he said, "friend has yummy toes
in bed. I take the jam and
spread it on my bread." "Ewww!
That's gross," I said. "How'd you
like it if I licked your toes
in bed?" "I'm sorry," said Ned
"but I must be fed some way
before bed."

Christopher Aneroussos, 11

I've always wondered why the snitzelbopper that lives under my bed licks my toes at night. I caught him once and gave him quite a fright. He jumped, hopped, meowed, barked and scurried under my bed. At that point I was sure I should call him Ned. "Friend, friend, friend," he said, "friend has yummy toes in bed. I take the jam and spread it on my bread." "Ewww! That's gross," I said. "How'd you like it if I licked your toes in bed?" "I'm sorry," said Ned, "but I must be fed some way before bed."

Christopher Aneroussos, Age 11, Brampton, On
Earncliffe Senior Public School

I've always wondered if there was such a thing as God, or if it was just a belief that people made up to worship. I am caught in between believing and not believing. There is no actual proof of existence or non-existence. Even though I was taught to believe, I can't seem to. I attend church as much as possible and this year, after last year's confirmation, I will be serving the church and its people. So here's a question I would like answered, do you believe?

Meagan Baker, Age 12, Grand Bank, NL
Lake Academy

I've always wondered where the northern lights come from. They dance in the sky like they are movie stars. The Polar Bears are admiring them at the drive-thru. They want all the world to see their dance as they tour from city to city. Purple, green and pink shades create their costume. Maybe tomorrow they will shine upon me. Whenever it happens, I hope it lands on the weekend, because I would stay up all night. My little sister would be afraid, but I would keep her eyes open for the performance that never repeats itself the same way again.

Nicolette Bala, Age 8

I've always wondered where the Northern Lights came from. They dance in the sky like they are movie stars. The polar bears are admiring them at the drive-thru. They want all the world to see their dance as they tour from city to city. Purple, green and pink shades create their costume. Maybe tomorrow they will shine upon me. Whenever it happens, I hope it lands on the weekend, because I would stay up all night. My little sister would be afraid, but I would keep her eyes open for the performance that never repeats itself the same way again.

Nicolette Bala, Age 8, Winnipeg, MB
Sister MacNamara

"I've always wondered where rainbows come from." Ms. Blueberry said to her kindergarten class. "I know teacher! It's because someone very tall is throwing flower petals in the sky!" Sunita shouted. "No! It is because someone thought the sky was paper and they drew on it!" Sarmad exclaimed. "It's because fireworks exploded!", said Milan. "A giant bent a big colourful tree!", said Peter. "It's candy from a pinata!", said Fernando. "No! You're all wrong! It's light shining through water droplets!" Amanda was outraged! The entire class turned to stare at her. "WHAT?!" They shouted.
The End

Olivia Isajev-Balanyk Age 11

"I've always wondered where rainbows come from." Ms. Blueberry said to her kindergarten class. "I know teacher! It's because someone very tall is throwing flower petals in the sky!" Sunita shouted. "No! It is because someone thought the sky was paper and they drew on it!" Sarmad exclaimed. "It's because fireworks exploded!" said Milan. "A giant bent a big colourful tree!" said Peter. "It's a candy from a pinata!" said Fernando. "No! You're all wrong! It's light shining through water droplets!" Amanda was outraged! The entire class turned to star at her "What?!" they shouted.

Olivia Isajev-Balanyk, Age 11, Etobicoke, ON
Humber Valley Village

I've always wondered what it would be, like to go the extra mile. Would go be happy, sad, scared, or glad? How many people would I see with the same goals and ambitions as me? I would like to feel that I can sing as loud, dance as much, and run as fast as I'd like. I want to try and help people in need and get rid of terrorism, poverty and greed. I'd like to show the world that no one needs to frown, even if you've made a mistake, it's not too late to turn your life around.

Karley Barnard, age 11

I've always wondered what it would be like to go the extra mile. Would I be happy, sad, scared or glad? How many people would I see with the same goals and ambitions as me? I would like to feel that I can sing as loud, dance as much and run as fast as I'd like. I want to try and help people in need and get rid of terrorism, poverty and greed. I'd like to show the world that no one needs to frown, even if you've made a mistake, it's not too late to turn your life around.

Karley Barnard, Age 11, Winnipeg, MB
Sun Valley School

I've always wondered where the wind blows or why the grass grows. What happens to balloons when they drift to the sky, or why innocent people suddenly die. And where do they go? Nobody knows. Is there a man, up in the moon? Or why do birds fly, like the majestic loon? Where does time go? As we play away. Why are things boring on some long days? No one knows why things happen as they do. So live each day, As it's something new. Everything's good if you put on a smile, and read my poem once in awhile!

Sara Barwin, 12 yrs

I've always wondered where the wind blows or why the grass grows. What happens to balloons when they drift to the sky or why innocent people suddenly die. And where do they go? Nobody knows. Is there a man, up in the moon? Or why do birds fly, like the majestic loon? Where does time go? As we play away, why are things boring on some long days? No one know why things happen as they do, so live each day as it's something new. Everything's good if you put on a smile, and read my poem once in a while!

Sara Barwin, Age 12, Langley, BC
James Hill Elementary

Je me suis toujours demandé si les lutins réparaient les souliers des petits enfants mals chaussés. Et s'ils venaient chez-moi ce midi pour réparer mes espadrilles d'extérieures ? La cloche annonce que midi est arrivé. Je prends le petit autobus jaune qui me reconduit chez-moi. Avec grande stupeur j'ouvre la porte de ma chambre. Je découvre deux mignons petits lutins qui réparent mes chaussures. Ils sont eux très surpris. Je m'écroule sur le sol. Je me réveille, mes souliers sont réparés mais les lutins : disparus. Sûrement pour prendre soin de d'autres chaussures. Qui sait ?

Ariane Béland   10 ans

Je me suis toujours demandé si les lutins réparaient les souliers des petits enfants mal chaussés. Et s'ils venaient chez moi ce midi pour réparer mes espadrilles d'extérieur ? La cloche annonce que midi est arrivé. Je prends le petit autobus jaune qui me reconduit chez moi. Avec grande stupeur j'ouvre la porte de ma chambre. Je découvre deux mignons petits lutins qui réparent mes chaussures. Ils sont eux très surpris. Je m'écroule sur le sol. Je me réveille, mes souliers sont réparés mais les lutins : disparus. Sûrement pour prendre soin de d'autres chaussures. Qui sait ?

Ariane Béland, 10 ans, Rivière-du-Loup, QC
École Joly

I've always wondered why cat's and dog's don't like each other. I have noticed when I go over to My friend's house they have a dog and cat but you never see them play with each other. Maybe it's because Cat's are so grossed out by dog's like the way they eat like we all Know dog's are sloppy and Cats are not. Dog's think they are good hunters but really they're not. Cats are. Dog's either get picks all over from a porcupine or are attacked by some other bigger animal. Dog's just don't Know when to quit.

Clarissa Bennett, 12

I've always wondered why cats and dogs don't like each other. I have noticed when I go over to my friend's house they have a dog and cat but you never see them play with each other. Maybe it's because cats are so grossed out by dogs like the way they eat like we all know dogs are sloppy and cats are not. Dogs think they are good hunters but really they're not. Cats are. Dogs either get picks all over from a porcupine or are attacked by some of the bigger animals. Dogs just don't know when to quit!

Clarissa Bennett, Age 12, Sault-Ste.-Marie, ON
Blind River Public School

I've always wondered if life is nothing but a one night dream, if our very existence relies on the sleeping of an individual. Perhaps when we die, that person has woken up and we are simply taken out of the world; or maybe, when we sleep, they wake, and when we wake, they sleep. We might be in dreams, all connected and relying upon each other. Maybe, in the black darkness of night, when we put our heads onto the pillows and pull the covers over our heads and doze off, we too are creating a world for someone.

Gabbi Bernard, Age 12, Sherwood Park, AB
Cloverbar Junior High School

Je me suis toujours demandé pourquoi les sentiments existaient-ils ? Sûrement pour ajouter un peu de piquant à la vie ! Que serait la mort sans tristesse ou bien un anniversaire sans joie ? Une multitude de moments deviendraient intéressants sans les sentiments ! Un film d'horreur sans frissons et sueurs. Une dispute sans colère… C'est aussi une façon de s'exprimer. Notre vie serait aussi terne que si on mimait tout à la place d'agir réellement. Pour conclure, je n'ai qu'une phrase à vous dire : « Continuez d'être ému, surpris, horrifié, triste, amoureux, généreux, heureux mais ne soyez jamais un être sans aucune émotion. »

Harold Jean Bernatchez, 12 ans, Rimouski, QC
École St-Jean

28

I've always wondered why trees grow so tall. Why are they not like weeds, helpless and small? They could be like flowers, colours are bright, they could be like thorns, ready to fight. Oaks are tall, large and wise, while poplars are usually known for their size. Apples are cheery but never mean, they come in many colours like red and green. They are my great, amazing friends, whatever pain I might have, the trees always mends. I look at them now as I sit under their shade, and I am amazed at the glorious things that God has made.

Adam BESWICK 12

I've always wondered why trees grow so tall. Why are they not like weeds helpless and small? They could be like flowers, colours are bright. They could be like thorns ready to fight. Oaks are tall, large and wise, while poplars are usually known for their size. Apples are cheery but never mean, they come in many colours like red and green. They are my great amazing friends, whatever pain I might have, the trees always mends. I look at them now as I sit under their shade and I am amazed at the glorious things that God has made.

Adam Beswick, Age 12, Ilderton, ON
Oxbow Public School

I've always wondered what earth would be like if dogs ruled it. You're a dog, walking down the street. You pass "The doggie diner," and "Canine Clothes." Finally you reach H-U-M-A-N-S. You go in. Humans in cages line the walls. The prices are shocking so you leave. You head towards "The doggie diner." You enter, wait in line and finally it's your turn. You approach the counter, and order a "Pupsi." You pull three milk bones from your pocket. You grab your "Pupsi" and drink it… So that's what our world would be like if dogs ruled it.

Haley Bielinski, Age 10, St. Andrews, MB
École Riverbend Community School

I've always wondered why nobody ever talks to me. As soon as I cautiously approach a rabbit, it bounds away. The bull moose don't stick around for conversation either. Just yesterday, I carefully crept up to one and it bolted, as if something was after it! It couldn't have been more than two days ago, when I quietly padded up to a herd of white-tailed deer. They were gone in a blink of an eye, not one willing to chat with me. How can they resist my glistening, white smile? Yep, being a cougar can get pretty lonely sometimes.

Landon Black, 12

I've always wondered why nobody ever talks to me. As soon as I cautiously approach a rabbit, it bounds away. The bull moose don't stick around for conversation either. Just yesterday, I carefully crept up to one and it bolted, as if something was after it! It couldn't have been more than two days ago, when I quietly padded up to a herd of white-tailed deer. They were gone in a blink of an eye, not one willing to chat with me. How can they resist my glistening, white smile? Yep, being a cougar can get pretty lonely sometimes.

Landon Black, Age 12, New Lowell, ON
New Lowell Central Public

I've always wondered how dreams come to us. Do they come from our mind or do they come from God? Do they come from something you worry about? Maybe they come from your dreamcatcher. It keeps the bad ones in, but sometimes the nightmares get out. Maybe the clouds make them and comes through the window. Maybe the stars make them and send them down to you and go through our mind. Maybe the wind makes them and blows them to you. I've always wondered why we dream.

Jayden ~~Bohn~~ age 8

I've always wondered how dreams come to us. Do they come from our mind or do they come from God? Do they come from something you worry about? Maybe they come from your dreamcatcher. It keeps the bad ones in but sometimes the nightmares get out. Maybe the clouds makes them and come through the window. Maybe the stars make them and send them down to you and go through your mind. Maybe the wind makes them and blows them to you. I've always wondered why we dream.

Jayden Bohn, Age 8, Furdale, SK
South Corman Park School

I've always Wondered where words came from. I know the Caveman did'nt come up with words because they groaned. At least I think they did. Did words come from the pictures on caves and people just made up words for them? When the Caveman died and more people came to life, did someone wake up one day and start to speak? Or did aliens from outer space teach people how to talk? It has always been a mystery to me and probably a lot of other people. The mystery of where words came from is something I've always wondered about.

Shawnee Bomberry Age 10

I've always wondered where words came from. I know the caveman didn't come up with words because they groaned. At least I think they did. Did words come from the pictures on caves and people just made up words for them? When the caveman died and more people came to life, did someone wake up one day and start to speak? Or did aliens from outer space teach people how to talk? It has always been a mystery to me and probably a lot of other people. The mystery of where words came from is something I've always wondered about.

Shawnee Bomberry, Age 10, Hagersville, ON
Oliver M. Smith School

Je me suis toujours demandé si les voeux se réalisent un jour. Est-ce vrai que lorsqu'on souffle les bougies de notre gâteau, regarde une étoile filante passer dans la nuit étoilée, trouve un sou noir, jette de la monnaie dans une fontaine, lorsque l'on trouve un trèfle à quatre feuilles et toutes les autres affirmations de ce genre ! Nos voeux vont se réaliser ? On l'espère ! En tout cas, ce sera toujours la clef du mystère !

Katrine Bonnette – 11 ans

Je me suis toujours demandé si les voeux se réalisent un jour. Est-ce vrai que lorsqu'on souffle les bougies de notre gâteau, regarde une étoile filante passer dans la nuit étoilée, trouve un sou noir, jette de la monnaie dans une fontaine, lorsque l'on trouve un trèfle à quatre feuilles et toutes les autres affirmations de ce genre ! Nos voeux vont se réaliser ? On l'espère ! En tout cas, ce sera toujours la clef du mystère !

Katrine Bonnette, 11 ans, Granby, QC
École Avé-Maria

Je me suis toujours demandé, pourquoi les nuages sont si comiques. L'été arrive, je me couche dans l'herbe en avant de mon domicile. Je contemple pendant des heures et des heures, ces grosses ouates blanches. Ceux-ci s'amusent à cache-cache, à se transformer en fantôme et à me jouer des tours. Ils disparaissent pour réapparaître en chat, chien. Le soir tombant, tous ces cumulus regagnent leur lit, fatigués de leur journée. Je suis toujours là, à regarder les étoiles. Maman m'appelle: "Colin, vient rêver dans ton lit." Je ferme les yeux et je savoure cette douceur de la vie.

Colin Bordeleau 10 ans

Je me suis toujours demandé pourquoi les nuages sont si comiques. L'été arrivé, je me couche dans l'herbe en avant de mon domicile. Je contemple pendant des heures et des heures, ces grosses ouates blanches. Ceux-ci s'amusent à cache-cache, à se transformer en fantôme et à me jouer des tours. Ils disparaissent pour réapparaître en chat, chien. Le soir tombant, tous ces cumulus regagnent leur lit, fatigués de leur journée. Je suis toujours là à regarder les étoiles. Maman m'appelle « Colin, viens rêver dans ton lit. » Je ferme les yeux et je savoure cette douceur de la vie.

Colin Bordeleau, 10 ans, Grand-Mère, QC
École Antoine-Hallé

I've always wondered why the winds always go around objects and never through. I've always wondered why they blow so strong and then quiet down. Why do they appear so suddenly and then die down to nothing? I wonder many other things but I ponder upon this matter the most of all. But now I stop all wondering and think, if I found all this out, there would be nothing to wonder about. I keep wondering but I never find the answer.

By:
Lacey Borstmayer
Age: 11

I've always wondered why the winds always go around objects and never through. I've always wondered why they blow so strong and then quiet down. Why do they appear so suddenly and then die down to nothing? I wonder many other things but I ponder upon this matter the most of all. But now I stop all wondering and think, if I found all this out, there would be nothing to wonder about. I keep wondering but I never find the answer.

Lacey Borstmayer, Age 11, Prairie River, SK
Stewart Hawke Elementary School

Je me suis toujours demandé ce qui faisait avancer les nuages.
Le vent assurément mais, ils aiment peut-être flotter, avancer,
courir, s'arrêter par eux-mêmes avec leurs petites pattes. Car
les nuages ressemblent parfois à des chevaux, des moutons,
des avions et j'ai même vu une fois un éléphant qui lorsqu'il
s'est mis à avancer et à avancer, est parti grâce aux vents saluer
de la trompe d'autres enfants. Oui vraiment, j'adore les nuages
avec un beau ciel bleu.

Samuel Boudreault, 9 ans, Ste-Rose-du-Nord, QC
École Ste-Rose

I've always wondered what it would be like to be a cheetah. Running extraordinarily fast through the jungle, leaping on my prey! Then after my hard days of work I would sleep on a beautiful bed of grass that would be so comfortable and cozy. There would be dangerous consequences being a cheetah like hunters, who would run after me and try to shoot me. They would never catch me though because I would be too fast for them! I think I would much rather be a human any day. Wouldn't you?

By: Melissa Brake / Age 12

I've always wondered what it would be like to be a cheetah. Running extraordinarily fast through the jungle, leaping on my prey! Then after my hard days of work I would sleep on a beautiful bed of grass that would be so comfortable and cozy. There would be dangerous consequences being a cheetah like hunters, who would run after me and try to shoot me. They would never catch me though because I would be too fast for them! I think I would much rather be a human any day. Wouldn't you?

Melissa Brake, Age 12, Corner Brook, NL
Presentation Junior High

I've always wondered how Purple people got purple. I heard of Pink Sky's, blue pigs, and even orange wolves, but purple people that' just crazy. I first saw purple people in a dream I once had. Everyone was normal and then everyone turned purple. As I walked around my town, I noticed that everyone was purple. The mailman, police officers, and even all of the fire department. Then suddenly I woke up, I thought it was all just a bad dream, but then when I went outside everyone was purple, and I always wondered how purple people got purple.

Michael Brown   Age. 12

I've always wondered how Purple people got purple. I heard of pink skies, blue pigs and even orange wolves, but purple people that's just crazy. I first saw purple people in a dream I once had. Everyone was normal and then everyone turned purple. As I walked around my town, I noticed that everyone was purple. The mailman, police officers, and even all of the fire department. Then suddenly I woke up, I thought it was all just a bad dream, but then when I went outside everyone was purple, and I always wondered how purple people got purple.

Michael Brown, Age 12, Sussex, NB
Sussex Middle School

I've always wondered how an animal's mind works. Scientists have theories, but how can they be proven? I mean have scientists ever been animals, can they talk to animals? It seems to me that these are the only ways that these speculations can be proven. Do animals think? What passes through their minds? Is it images or ideas, and how much are they aware of? Hmm...? I guess this is one of those mysteries that you can wonder about, but never really find the answer. I guess the animal world will keep its secrets after all!

Jenel Brûlé, Age 12

I've always wondered how an animal's mind works. Scientists have theories, but how can they be proven? I mean have scientists ever been animals, can they talk to animals? It seems to me that these are only ways that these speculations can be proven. Do animals think? What passes through their minds? Is it images or ideas, and how much are they aware of? Hmm..? I guess this is one of those mysteries that you can wonder about, but never really find the answer. I guess the animal world will keep its secrets after all!

Jenel Brûlé, Age 12, Notre-Dame-de-l'île-Perrot, QC
St. Thomas High School

I've Always Wondered about time. Are there masters or people who control time? Does time have secrets, memories or mysteries? Mabey there will be a time machine – a machine where I would visit the dinosaurs and even catch a ride! Then I would visit the pioneers and run freely through the fields of Ancient Greece. Lastly, I would visit the medieval times and watch jousting competitions and feast at night. Then I would leave the past, and go back home to what is even more important and fun–my family and home.

Chandler Buchanan Age:11

I've always wondered about time. Are there masters or people who control time? Does time have secrets, memories, or mysteries? Maybe there will be a time machine – a machine where I would visit the dinosaurs and even catch a ride! Then I would visit the pioneers and run freely through the fields of Ancient Greece. Lastly, I would visit the medieval times and watch jousting competitions and feast at night. Then I would leave the past, and go back home to what is even more fun – my family and home.

Chandler Buchanan, Age 11, Toronto, ON
De La Salle College

I've always wondered why do lady bugs have black spots? Why not blue spots, green spots or even pink. How'd they get them? Maybe while the lady bug was flying it fell into black paint. Maybe a little kid caught a lady bug and thought it was plain, so they took a marker and drew dots. It would be funny if they had no spots at all, but that would be too plain. What about if they had triangles or even stars, instead of dots? That would make me laugh! Who knows why they have spots, it'll be a mystery.

Amanda Robyn J. Bundoc Age. 11

I've always wondered why do ladybugs have black spots? Why not blue spots, green spots or even pink? How'd they get them? Maybe while the ladybug was flying it fell into black paint. Maybe a little kid caught a ladybug and thought it was plain, so they took a marker and drew dots. It would be funny if they had no spots at all, but that would be too plain. What about if they had triangles or even stars, instead of dots? That would make me laugh! Who knows why they have spots, it'll be a mystery.

Amanda Robyn J. Bundoc, Age 11, Mississauga, ON
St. Albert of Jerusalem

I've always wondered why my lizard was purple. When I bought him, he was green. I would feed him grapes and crickets every day. He really liked the grapes. After a while, I saw that he was changing. I woke up one morning and screamed "AHHHHHH! My lizard is purple!!!" I was worried sick! I brought my lizard to the vet. He checked him over, and told me that my pet wasn't just any lizard. It was a purple leaping lizard! It wasn't the grapes after all! My lizard was almost full grown. "Whew!" I love my new purple lizard.

Bret Butler, Age 9

I've always wondered why my lizard was purple. When I bought him, he was green. I would feed him grapes and crickets every day. He really liked the grapes. After a while, I saw that he was changing. I woke up one morning and screamed "AHHHHHH! My lizard is purple!" I was worried sick! I brought my lizard to the vet. He checked him over and told me that my pet wasn't just any lizard, it was a purple leaping lizard! It wasn't the grapes after all! My lizard was almost full grown. "Whew!" I love my new purple lizard.

Bret Butler, Age 9, Chatham, ON
Home-schooled

I've always wondered if there is a pot of gold at the end of the rainbow. Would the gold be real? Or maybe it would be chocolate gold? How long would it take to climb the long rainbow? I wonder, would you fall off the rainbow while climbing back down? If you fell would you land on a cloud? If you did, how would you get back down to ground? Would you be stuck up there your whole life? Or would a plane come and rescue you? If they did, would you go and try to get the gold again?

Jalyn Callele, Age 10, Lloydmister, AB
St. Mary's Elementary School

44

I've always wondered how many stars beautifully light up the lonesome dark sky. How many shine up high joyfully dancing together hand in hand. The amount of stars playing with the big round moon singing songs in harmony. The night would look so sad and lonely that we would all be afraid. But, no the little cheerful dots twinkle away every night glad to share their peacefullness while the world sleeps calmly, but, one question will still remain, how many Float while we sleep.

Carolina Campos ♡ 11

I've always wondered how many stars beautifully light up the lonesome dark sky. How many shine up high joyfully dancing together hand in hand. The amount of stars playing with the big round moon singing songs in harmony. The night would look so sad and lonely that we would all be afraid. But, no, the little cheerful dots twinkle away every night glad to share their peacefullness while the world sleeps calmly, but one question will still remain, how many float while we sleep?

Carolina Campos, Age 11, Mississauga, ON
St. Rose of Lima

Je me suis toujours demandé comment font les magasins pour donner des prix aux articles. Une fois, je me promenais dans un centre commercial avec mes parents. J'ai vu une statue de chat qui coûtait deux mille dollars. Je voulais la mettre dans ma chambre. Alors j'ai montré la statue à ma mère mais elle était trop chère. Rendu chez moi je suis allé dans ma chambre et je me suis dit qu'une statue de chat ça ne vaut pas deux mille dollars. Un jour, j'aimerais bien fixer moi-même les prix des produits.

Je me suis toujours demandé comment font les magasins pour donner des prix aux articles. Une fois, je me promenais dans un centre commercial avec mes parents. J'ai vu une statue de chat qui coûtait deux mille dollars. Je voulais la mettre dans ma chambre. Alors j'ai montré la statue à ma mère mais elle était trop cher. Rendu chez moi je suis allé dans ma chambre et je me suis dit qu'une statue de chat ça ne vaut pas deux mille dollars. Un jour, j'aimerais bien fixer moi-même les prix des produits.

Alex Carrière, 11 ans, St. Charles de Bellechasse, QC
École de l'Étincelle

I've always wondered why I'm not good at Math? Math is hard for me because I don't learn Math at home. I don't know timestables I only know up to one. I've always wished that I was good at Math. I never wanted to do hard, hard Math because I'm not that good at Math. My mom scolds me because I don't get my math done. I've always wondered Why there's such a thing as math? I wish I wish Math was not made up. I don't know why teachers know math but kids don't know that much. I Wish Math was like Art.

Michelle Castro, 9

I've always wondered why I'm not good at math. Math is hard for me because I don't learn math at home. I don't know timestables, I only know up to one. I always wished that I was good at math. I never wanted to do hard, hard math because I'm not that good at math. My mom scolds me because I don't get my math done. I always wondered why there's such a thing as math? I wish math was not made up. I don't know why teachers know math but kids don't know that much.
I wish math was like art.

Michelle Castro, Age 9, Windsor, ON
Malborough

I've always wondered... "What if everything adults told children came true?" Millions of children would have no teeth because "teeth fall out if you eat too much candy!" How many of us would walk around with permanent pouts because "your face will stay like that if you keep pouting!" Chocolate bars with legs would walk around town because "you become what you eat!" Imagine seeing mothers use the bags under their children's eyes to carry groceries because their children stayed up too late and got shopping bags under their eyes? Thank goodness adults don't say what they mean!

Zamyla Morgan Chan, Age 11, Vancouver, BC
Sir William Osler Elementary

I've always wondered how it would feel to be a melody, to have my own rhythm, beat and tune? I would have a part for each of my favorite instruments the violin, picalo, and harp. The majestic flute would trill to the lead! What type of music would I be jazz rock or country? No I would be one of Mozant's greatest pieces! I could make people feel whatever I wanted! I could make them feel excitement, joy, or sorrow! I am unique, without me the world would be bleak. I am music!

Alexandra christman age 9

I've always wondered how it would feel to be a melody, to have my own rhythm, beat and tune? I would have a part for each of my favourite instruments, the violin, piccolo, and harp. The majestic flute would trill to the lead. What type of music would I be, jazz, rock or country? No I would be one of Mozart's greatest pieces! I could make people feel whatever I wanted! I could make them feel excitement, joy or sorrow! I am unique, without me the world would be bleak. I am music!

Alexandra Christman, Age 9, Spruce Grove, AB
Connections for Learning

I've always wondered what does the tooth fairy
do with all those teeth? Does she make them into
necklaces? Does she use them for magic
potions? Or does she collect them just for fun?
Losing your first tooth is a very important day,
so tell everyone. Before you go to sleep put it under your pillow.
That very night, while you are sleeping, the tooth fairy flies into
your room. She carefully takes your tooth, and leaves behind
money or a special little present. Haven't you ever wondered
what she does with all those teeth? There must be millions!

Marco Ciavarella, Age 8, Burlington, ON
St. John School

204 Stories by Canadian Children
« Je me suis toujours demandé... » 204 nouvelles par des jeunes Canadiens

I've always wondered if the moon was really made of cheese, so yesterday, I went to investigate. I went to my very favourite scientist, Mr. Slimy. He lent me his cool rocket and went with me to the moon. Once we arrived at the moon I took a look around. It was so cool! It was white as snow and soft as a brand new pillow. When we arrived home Mr. Slimy went straight to his lab. A few minutes later Mr. Slimy told me something very, very shocking. The moon wasn't made of cheese, but yummy, gooey marshmallow. Mmmm!

Charlotte Coilan, Age 10, Coquitlam, BC
Nestor Elementary

I've always wondered what lingers in my sock drawer. My name's Tim, and here's my story. One morning I opened up my closet and saw a two foot tall flying dwarf. He ran into my sock drawer. The next day he did the same thing. This time, I followed him. We ended up in Happyville. There were rainbows, unicorns, dinosaurs named Chunky and Sylvester and flying pigs. The dwarf introduced himself. His name was Englebert. He told me everything about Happyville. Soon it was dinner. I bid farewell, and now I know that Happyville is in my sock drawer.

Brittany Crocker, 11 years

I've always wondered what lingers in my sock drawer. My name's Tim, and here's my story. One morning I opened up my closet and saw a two foot tall flying dwarf. He ran into my sock drawer. The next day he did the same thing. This time, I followed him. We ended up in Happyville. There were rainbows, unicorns, dinosaurs named Chunky and Sylvester and flying pigs. The dwarf introduced himself. His name was Englebert. He told me everything about Happyville. Soon it was dinner. I big farewell, and now I know that Happyville is in my sock drawer.

Brittany Crocker, Age 11, Burlington, ON
Ryerson

I've always wondered where a bird goes for the winter. They probably go to Hawaii and stay at the Seagull Hotel. The Seagull Hotel has a huge pool with a diving board. I wonder if they use suntan lotion or wear little sunhats? They probably rent nests to sleep in. I can see them now, feasting on worm-a-ghetti while drinking slug slurpees. At night they might go to the Bald Eagle Ball and do the flamingo! When their vacation is over, they'll have to pack up there little backpacks and fly back home. The exercise will be worth it.

Cadence Currie, age 8

I've always wondered where a bird goes for the winter. They probably go to Hawaii and stay at the Seagull Hotel. The Seagull Hotel has a huge pool with a diving board. I wonder if they use suntan lotion or wear little sun hats? They probably rent nests to sleep in. I can see them now, feasting on worm-a-ghetti while drinking slug slurpees. At night they might go to the Bald Eagle Ball and do the flamingo! When their vacation is over, they'll have to pack up their little backpacks and fly back home. The exercise will be worth it.

Cadence Currie, Age 8, Toronto, ON
Centennial Road Junior Public School

I've always wondered why the crimson leaves of fall wave to the whispering wind which cools the copper sky, an icy glare screams at the return of the silver flakes of dancing snow. I've always wondered why the berries once gold now only a chestnut form, skies once filled with song now dead with the quiet of the night. The days end quickly, the night ever so long. No time to wonder. Why do the willows weep at each fallen sepal, why do the larks cease their song? Surely something is occurring. The snowy air is frozen. Winter has come!

Niki Cuthill, Age 10, Three Hills, AB
Prairie Christian Academy

I've always wondered what it is like
in a perfect world. Where the sky is
always blue and everyone is nice to you
You'll never find a mark on the road, just
maybe my old friend toad. There are
self-cleaning cars and bright, glowing
stars. When you laugh, the world laughs
When you smile, the world smiles.
Everyone wakes up happy, grinning from
ear to ear. There is never any fear. No
one delivers bad news, tears are only
for few. There are no robberies. The
world is based on love and peace.
Congeniality and kindness is a
given!

Olivia D'Alessandro, 11

I've always wondered what it is like in a perfect world. Where
the sky is always blue and everyone is nice to you. You'll never
find a mark on the road; just maybe my old friend toad. There are
self-cleaning cars and bright, glowing stars. When you laugh,
the world laughs. When you smile, they world smiles. Everyone
wakes up happy, grinning from ear to ear. There is never any
fear. Noone delivers bad news, tears are only for few. There are
no robberies. The world is based on love and peace. Congeniality
and kindness is a given!

Olivia D'Alessandro, Age 11, Mississauga, ON
St. Thomas Moore

I've always wondered what life would be like without gravity. I would float to the clouds made of cotton candy, grab some for my friends and for my family. All would be great, until it would hit me: but what about getting back down on the ground? How would it be possible? Then, I would look at my mom. To me she is Superwoman. So she would hold my hand and bring me back down. I would never let go of her hand. So I've often wondered how the love of your mother can always keep you grounded, so secure.

Kaylin Davison, 10 yrs

I've always wondered what life would be like without gravity. I would float to the clouds made of cotton candy, grab some for my friends and for my family. All would be great, until it would hit me: but what about getting back down on the ground? How would it be possible? Then, I would look at my mom. To me she is Superwoman. So she would hold my hand and bring me back down. I would never let go of her hand. So I've often wondered how the love of your mother can always keep you grounded, so secure.

Kaylin Davison, Age 10, Mississauga, ON
René-Lamoureux

I've always wondered what goes on inside clouds. Are they filled with cotton candy? Are they bright and loud? Are there unicorns, mermaids, pixies and elves? What goes on in there must be too magical to think up ourselves! Do they serve never-ending desserts like chocolate fudge and smarties? Do they play loud music and hold never-ending parties? Does everyone float freely without a care? I'd give anything to know what happens up there! Away from the sight of humans and birds, what goes on inside clouds must be too great for words!

Rebecca Dawe, 13

I've always wondered what goes on inside clouds. Are they filled with cotton candy? Are they bright and loud? Are there unicorns, mermaids, pixies and elves? What goes on in there must be too magical to think up ourselves. Do they serve never-ending desserts like chocolate fudge and smarties? Do they play loud music and hold never-ending parties? Does everyone float freely without a care? I'd give anything to know what happens up there! Away from the sight of humans and birds what goes on inside clouds must be too great for words.

Rebecca Dawe, Age 13, Scarborough, ON
Joseph Brant

I've always wondered how the very first animal was made? Could it be that when it rained, it carried a bean that was dropped and became an animal? Many people wonder, but does anyone really know? Maybe there was a lightning bolt in which an animal fell from the sky? Or perhaps it appeared out of nowhere? Even the most experienced scientist has no clue! There may be a witness that passed it down through generations. Many people tell stories of how they think the first animal was made, but what really happened, we may never know.......

Diana De Santis, age 11

I've always wondered how the very first animal was made? Could it be that when it rained it carried a bean that was dropped and became an animal? Many people wonder but does anyone really know? Maybe there was a lightning bolt in which an animal fell from the sky? Or perhaps it appeared out of nowhere? Even the most experienced scientist has no clue! There may be a witness that passed it down through generations. Many people tell stories of how they think the first animal was made but what really happened we may never know…

Diana De Santis, Age 11, Toronto, ON
Metro Prep Academy

I've always wondered what the tooth fairy does with all those teeth. I suppose she makes castles out of them, or maybe she makes them into tooth necklaces. Maybe she has a secret tunnel that goes to all the places on earth and back to her castle. Maybe her shoes are made from teeth. I've also always wondered how she knows when to pick up the teeth. Maybe she has a radar system in her castle. We'll never know what she looks like, but my two front teeth are loose so I'll get a visit from the fairy really soon.

Mackenzie Dever – Age 7

I've always wondered what the tooth fairy does with all those teeth. I suppose she makes castles out of them, or maybe she makes them into tooth necklaces. Maybe she has a secret tunnel that goes to all the places on earth and back to her castle. Maybe her shoes are made from teeth. I've also always wondered how she knows when to pick up the teeth. Maybe she has a radar system in her castle. We'll never know what she looks like, but my two front teeth are loose so I'll get a visit from the fairy really soon.

Mackenzie Dever, Age 7, Bobcaygeon, ON
Home-schooled

I've always wondered how I see so much of our huge planet through these small eyes of mine. Perhaps it is because I have travelled to many different parts of the globe and seen these places in person. Maybe it's because when I read different books and watch television I also learn much about the world just as if I was there in person. Perhaps it's because my mind is open to receiving all this information and knowledge that my eyes allows into my brain. Luckily, the world is so vast, that it'll always have something for my little eyes to see.

Daniela Di Geso, age 10

I've always wondered how I see so much of our huge planet through these small eyes of mine. Perhaps it is because I have travelled to many different parts of the globe and seen these places in person. Maybe it's because when I read different books and watch television I also learn much about the world just as if I was there in person. Perhaps it's because my mind is open to receiving all this information and knowledge that my eyes allow into my brain. Luckily, the world is so vast, that it'll always have something for my little eyes to see.

Daniela Di Geso, Age 10, Toronto, ON
Lambton Kingsways Junior Middle School

I've always wondered if little people live in the dryer because there is always a sock missing. What do they do with the socks? Do they make clothes, maybe they sell them. Who do they sell them to? Maybe they sell them to leprechauns or maybe they sell them to the Borrowers because little people are always friends with each other. It takes the little people so long to get to the Borrowers (it takes about 2 days) because they have such small steps. Wouldn't that be fun living in the dryer, taking socks, then selling them to the Borrowers?

Emily DiNardo 11yrs old

I've always wondered if little people live in the dryer because there is always a sock missing. What do they do with the socks? Do they make clothes, maybe they sell them. Who do they sell them to? Maybe they sell them to leprechauns or maybe they sell them to the Borrowers because little people are always friends with each other. It takes the little people so long to get to the Borrowers (it takes about 2 days) because they have such small steps. Wouldn't that be fun living in the dryer, taking socks, then selling them to the Borrowers?

Emily DiNardo, Age 11, St. Clare, ON
St. Clare School

I've always wondered how I ended up at the Boston aquarium. I'm here with about seventy-two other penguins, some are from the Arctic and I'm from Australia. My name is Peter the penguin! I have yellow and black hair and red eyes. All of my older brothers and older sisters are home or are in an aquarium like me. Each day about seven people come into the water to clean up after us and the best part is the super yummy fish. They're bringing the fish, got to go! The yummy fishies are going in my tummy!

Haley Donald, Age 11, Halifax, NS
École Rockingham School

I've always wondered what it would be like to be a mother, to have a darling little dear to take care of, a cute little sweetheart with bright eyes and an adorable smile to gently rock to sleep. Tiny little hands would tightly squeeze my finger. My baby would be a sweet little bundle of joy. I would wrap her carefully in blankets when going out, and again at bed time, and as she closed her eyes in peaceful sleep I would hold her delicate little hand and happily gaze contently at my beautiful gift from Heaven.

Elizabeth Douitsis, Age 12, Toronto, ON
God Spoke Christian Academy

I've always wondered what life would be like if we could stop, pause, rewind and fast forward! Of course the annoying people who talk a lot will have a mute button. Maybe if we made a big mistake we could go back and fix it, and if you needed a break from life you could pause it and have a rest. But maybe we are better off how we are, learning important life lessons as we go through good times and bad, when we are happy or sad. I am sure we will get through life if we try to.

Rachel Drummond, Age 11, Salt Spring Island, BC
Queen of Angels School

Je me suis toujours demandé...
Si les humains pouvaient voler, si j'en
aurais la possibilité, j'irais explorer les
grandes vallées. Je planerais comme un
pélican, au dessus des vastes océans.
L'univers me semblerais plus grand.
La vie serait plus belle. Je volerais
comme une hirondelle. Tambourinant
de mes propres ailes. Ha! Quelle belle
vie d'oiseau! Que de chanter si haut!
Bien pelotonné dans mon nid,
j'observerais les étoiles la nuit. De la
Grèce à l'Italie je découvrirais l'art
des coloris. Pour terminer cet agréable
périple, je m'emporterais comme cet
oiseau. Rêvant d'amour et de liberté.
Espérant qu'un jour je volerais...

Carole-Anne Ducharme 9ans

Je me suis toujours demandé si les humains
pouvaient voler, si j'en aurais la possibilité j'irais
explorer les grandes vallées. Je planerais comme
un pélican, au-dessus des vastes océans. L'univers
me semblerait plus grand. La vie serait plus belle.
Je volerais comme une hirondelle, tambourinant de mes propres
ailes. Ha ! Quelle belle vie d'oiseau ! Que de chanter si haut !
Bien pelotonné dans mon nid, j'observerais les étoiles la nuit.
De la Grèce à l'Italie je découvrirais l'art des coloris. Pour
terminer cet agréable périple, je m'emporterais comme cet oiseau.
Rêvant d'amour et de liberté. Espérant qu'un jour je volerais.

Carole-Anne Ducharme, 9 ans, Kingsley Falls, QC
École Cascatelle

Je me suis toujours demandé... pourquoi ma tante Jina est frisée de partout? Avant ma tante avait les cheveux plats, plats, plats et elle escaladait souvent le Mont-Ressort. Un jour elle est allée plus haut que toutes les autres fois mais, elle est tombée. Au sol il y avait pleins de ressorts électriques et elle est tombée tête première dessus. Elle a pogné un choc électrique et elle est restée frisée toute sa vie. Maintenant tout le monde l'appelle frisotte la rigolotte. Va-t-elle encore escalader le Mont-Ressort? La prochaine fois elle va peut-être aller au Mont-Rasoir!

FIN!

Alex-Anne Duchesne 11ans

Je me suis toujours demandé pourquoi ma tante Jina est frisée de partout ? Avant ma tante avait les cheveux plats, plats, plats, et elle escaladait souvent le Mont-Ressort. Un jour elle est allée plus haut que toutes les autres fois. Mais, elle est tombée. Au sol il y avait plein de ressorts électriques. Et elle est tombée tête première dessus. Elle a pogné un choc électrique et elle est restée frisée toute sa vie. Maintenant tout le monde l'appelle frisotte la rigolotte. Va-t-elle encore escalader le Mont-Ressort ? La prochaine fois elle va peut-être aller au Mont-Rasoir !

Alex-Anne Duchesne, 11 ans, St-Ambroise, QC
Collège St-Ambroise

I've always wondered why school buses are yellow. My question was answered when I heard about Charlie, the yellow school bus. One day after Charlie dropped the kids off at school, he decided he was tired of being yellow. Charlie went to a body shop and got painted multi-coloured. The next day, he went to pick up the children. When he got there, the children didn't recognize him. None of the children knew it was Charlie. They refused to board the bus. Charlie was so upset that he went back to being yellow. That's why school buses are yellow.

Julie Dunning, Age 12, Toronto, ON
St. Angela School

Je me suis toujours demandé comment se fait-il que notre cerveau soit capable de se souvenir de tout ce qu'on apprend à l'école. C'est beaucoup au fil des journées, en une semaine, en un mois... C'est un exploit ! De plus, se souvenir de presque tout jusqu'à notre mort, ça tient du miracle ! Comme j'aimerais pouvoir examiner un cerveau, connaître ses secrets, observer cette merveille ! Je réalise que notre cerveau est sûrement le plus perfectionné des ordinateurs. Comment puis-je en prendre soin et le garder en santé ?

Carolyne Dupuis, 11 ans

Je me suis toujours demandé comment se fait-il que notre cerveau soit capable de se souvenir de tout ce qu'on apprend à l'école. C'est beaucoup au fil des journées, en une semaine, en un mois… C'est un exploit ! De plus, se souvenir de presque tout jusqu'à notre mort, ça tient du miracle ! Comme j'aimerais pouvoir examiner un cerveau, connaître ses secrets, observer cette merveille ! Je réalise que notre cerveau est sûrement le plus perfectionné des ordinateurs. Comment puis-je en prendre soin et le garder en santé ?

Carolyne Dupuis, 10 ans, Sorel-Tracy, QC
École Laplume

Je me suis toujours demandé si les dragons avaient déjà existé ? Eh bien Oui ! Ecoutez l'histoire suivante. Dans un royaume lointain vivait un Roi très curieux. Il aimait se promener seul et explorer tous les recoins de son pays. Un jour il fit une découverte. Un drôle d'animal qui volait. Bizarre se disait le Roi. Serait-ce un dragon ? Mais non, tout le monde sait qu'ils n'existent pas. Mais voilà, c'en était un, un vrai de vrai. Et il se nommait Grégor. Le Roi et Grégor devinrent de bons amis. Ils vécurent beaucoup d'aventures ensemble. Un lien les unissait : L'amitié...

Océane Durand 10 ans

Je me suis toujours demandé si les dragons avaient déjà existé ?
Eh bien oui ! Écoutez l'histoire suivante. Dans un royaume
lointain, vivait un roi très curieux. Il aimait se promener seul
et explorer tous les recoins de son pays. Un jour il fit une
découverte. Un drôle d'animal qui volait. Bizarre, se disait
le roi, serait-ce un dragon ? Mais non, tous le monde sait
qu'ils n'existent pas. Mais voilà, c'en était un, un vrai de vrai.
Et il se nommait Grégor. Le roi et Grégor devinrent de bons
amis. Ils vécurent beaucoup d'aventures ensemble.
Un lien les unissait : L'amitié…

Océane Durand, 10 ans, Ste-Catherine-de-la-J.-C., QC
École Alexander-Wolff

I've always wondered what it would be like to have a remote control for time. It would have "pause", "play", "fast forward" and "rewind" buttons. I could relive a fun experience by using the "rewind" feature. The "pause" button would give me more time to answer questions on a test. And imagine, no more long car trips! I could use "fast forward" to get there right away! BUT, what if my remote malfunctioned? I might get stuck in "rewind" until prehistoric times! I might leave the world on "pause" forever! Maybe my remote isn't such a good idea after all...

Marina Durham, 12

I've always wondered what it would be like to have a remote control for time. It would have a "pause", "play", "fast forward" and "rewind" buttons. I could relive a fun experience using the "rewind" feature. The "pause" button would give me more time to answer questions on a test. And imagine, no more long car trips! I could use "fast forward" to be there right away!! BUT, what if my remote malfunctioned? I might get stuck in "rewind" until prehistoric times! I might leave the world on "pause" forever! Maybe my remote isn't such a good idea after all...

Marina Durham, Age 12, Coldstream, BC
Kelowna Christian School DEL

I've always wondered if honeybees were as big as elephants, the world would be a magical land. Full of rainbows and fun, for unicorns to dance upon. The horses would run free, through lush green grass. The flowers would grow as big as trees. Our vegetable gardens would be a bunnies heaven. The fruit we grow would be as sweet as Sugar cane. There would be lakes of sweet gold, for the bears to have their fill. The birds we see would fly so happily, looking down at me. The world would be so grand, in this magical dreamy land.

Stephanie Ennis, 12

I've always wondered if honeybees were as big as elephants, the world would be a magical land. Full of rainbows and fun, for unicorns to dance upon. The horses would run free, through lush green grass. The flowers would grow as big as trees. Our vegetable gardens would be a bunnies heaven. The fruit we grow would be as sweet as sugarcane. There would be lakes of sweet gold, for the bears to have their fill. The birds we see would fly so happily, looking down at me. The world would be so grand, in this magical dreamy land.

Stephanie Ennis, Age 12, Cultus Lake, BC
Vedder Middle School

I've always Wondered if I can Fly
Way up high in the sky. I Would race
through the clouds and go right through
the wind I Would fly to the Mountain
top of the highest Mountain in the world.
I would be famous, everybody would call me
Super Mitchell, I'd love that. And I would fly
to New Brunswic and find MY dear loving
MoM and bring her home with Me and
MY dad we'd go fishing and canoeing
together, and go to MY house together,
and we'd stay home till I aM gone.
That is what I've always Wondered.

Mitchell Evans age 11

I've always wondered if I can fly way up high in the sky. I would
race through the clouds and go right through the wind. I would fly
to the mountain top of the highest mountain in the world. I would
be famous, everybody would call me Super Mitchell. I'd love that.
And I would fly to New Brunswick and find my dear loving mom
and bring her home with me and my dad. We'd go fishing and
canoeing together and go to my house together and we'd stay
home, 'til I am gone. That is what I've always wondered.

Mitchell Evans, Age 11, Dartmouth, NB
John MacNeil School

I've always wondered Why deer hang out in the side of the highway? Don't their friends tell them what can happen? Why do they always wait until dusk, when it is hard to see them, to be on the road. Don't their Parents explain to them the dangers of such careless activities I've always wondered where they came from and what attracts them to the highway? Why do they run in front at cars at the last minute? I wish there was someone who could teach them to be careful out there!!

Magdalena Isabel Fast Age 12

I've always wondered why deer hang out in the side of the highway? Don't their friends tell them what can happen? Why do they always wait until dusk, when it is hard to see them to be on the road. Don't their parents explain to them the dangers of such careless activities! I've always wondered where they came from and what attracts them to the highway? Why do they run in front at cars at the last minute? I wish there was someone who could teach them to be careful out there.

Magdalena Isabel Fast, Age 12, Canal Flats, BC
Martin Morigeau Elementary

I've always wondered what it would be like to have a drawing
friend. You know, like a drawing that is your friend. I am going to
draw a nose... mouth... ears... hair... almost done. Now
I need arms, legs, and VOILA! "Hello," my drawing said. "Hi!
What is your name?", I asked. "Lucy!" She answered happily.
I had made a new friend. Two days later, the ink from her hand
started to fade away. "Uh oh!", she cried sadly. "I need to go back
to ink world or I'll disappear!" I was sad, but I let her go. "Bye!",
I exclaimed.

Hailey Faulks, Age 12, Abbotsford, BC
Chief Dan George

I've always wondered if pigs could fly. Then I would be able to ride them to school. And when the kids saw me, they would bring their pigs to school. Except one girl who doesn't have one and feels left out. So I would give her mine.

But then again, the place would be verry messy and we would have to clean up after. And instead of bird poop, it would be pig poop. And the principal would get mad because there would be pigs in the playground So it wouldnt be a good idea if pigs could fly.

Elizabeth Frans age 12

I've always wondered if pigs could fly. Then I would be able to ride them to school. And when the kids saw me, they would bring their pigs to school. Except one girl who doesn't have one and feels left out. So I would give her mine. But then again, the place would be very messy and we would have to clean up after. And instead of bird poop, it would be pig poop. And the principal would get mad because there would be pigs in the playground so it wouldn't be a good idea if pigs could fly.

Elizabeth Frans, Age 12, Toronto, ON
Earl Beatty School

I've always wondered, If I were dead
Would I float on a fluffy cloud bed?
Dancing and gliding, through the sky,
With a halo and wings, able to fly?

Or would I be buried, deep in the ground
With dirt all around me gritty and brown.
Would I be ash, kept in somebody's room,
Cold, gray, and fine, to be thrown away soon?

What I would give, to figure this out,
Being alive, to know all about,
BEING DEAD

Rachel Fung, 12

I've always wondered if I were dead, would I float on a fluffy cloud bed? Dancing and gliding, through the sky, with a halo and wings, able to fly? Or would I be buried, deep in the ground, with dirt all around me, gritty and brown. Would I be ash, kept in somebody's room. Cold, gray, and fine, to be thrown away soon? What I would give to figure this out, being alive to know all about, being dead.

Rachel Fung, Age 12, North Bay, ON
W.J. Fricker Public School

I've always wondered what it would be like to be two dimensional in a three dimensional world. I could slide under my sister's door and read her diary. I would always win hide-n-go-seek. I could get someone to fold me up like an airplane and throw me up in the air. Then I could finally fly. I could be my own bookmark. I could be my own toboggan. I could fold up into a paper boat and sail the seven seas. I could even be a lampshade. It would be so cool.

The End

Abbey Gagnon   Age: 11

I've always wondered what it would be like to be two dimensional in a three dimensional world. I could slide under my sister's door and read her diary. I would always win hide-n-go seek. I could get someone to fold me up like an airplane and throw me up in the air. Then I could finally fly. I could be my own bookmark. I could be my own toboggan. I could fold up into a paper boat and sail the seven seas. I could even be a lampshade. It would be so cool.
The End.

Abbey Gagnon, Age 11, Brampton, ON
Tall Pines School

Je me suis toujours demandé d'où vient la rosée du matin. Est-ce que c'est des petits lutins verts qui arrivent par dix ou par vingt peinturer d'edu votre gazon et vos fleurs? Peut-être que c'est les esprits de la nuit qui pleurent chaque matin? Ou encore il pleut des petites gouttes chaque soir...Est-ce que ça serait une machine conduite par des lutins noirs et maladroits nettoyerait les rues et un peu d'eau éclabousserait sur notre pelouse le matin avant le levée du soleil? Je pourrais sortir plein d'autres possibilités mais j'en aurais pour cette page...

Marie-Ève Gagnon 11 ans

Je me suis toujours demandé d'où vient la rosée du matin. Est-ce que c'est des petits lutins verts qui arrivent par dix ou par vingt, peinturer de l'eau sur votre gazon et vos fleurs ? Peut-être que c'est les esprits de la nuit qui pleurent chaque matin ? Ou encore il pleut des petites gouttes chaque soir… Est-ce que ça serait une machine conduite par des lutins noirs et maladroits nettoyerait les rues et un peu d'eau éclabousserait sur notre pelouse le matin avant la levée du soleil ? Je pourrais sortir plein d'autres possibilités, mais j'en aurais trop pour cette page…

Marie-Ève Gagnon, 11 ans, Maskinongé, QC
École St-Joseph

Je me suis toujours demandée, d'où venait le chocolat. Pourquoi avons-nous besoin de chocolat. Vous devez vous dire "parce que c'est bon." En avons-nous réellement besoin? Moi je suis sûre que le chocolat vient d'une planète : Le chocolat tombe-t-il du ciel comme la pluie? Non encore mieux. C'est une cigogne qui l'amène sur la terre, comme nous quand nous étions bébés. Arrive-t-il par vaisseau spatial? Les extraterrestres nous envoient-ils un cadeau de bienvenue? Un cadeau de bon voisinage. Ils sont polis nos amis les "aliennes", oui c'est ça qui a le plus de bon sens.

nom : Mathilde Gauthier-Larocque / âge : 11 ans

Je me suis toujours demandé d'où venait le chocolat. Pourquoi avons-nous besoin de chocolat. Vous devez vous dire « Parce que c'est bon ». En avons-nous réellement besoin ? Moi je suis sûre que le chocolat vient d'une planète. Le chocolat tombe-t-il du ciel comme la pluie ? Non, encore mieux. C'est une cigogne qui l'amène sur la terre, comme nous quand nous étions bébés. Arrive-t-il par vaisseau spatial ? Les extraterrestres nous envoient-ils un cadeau de bon voisinage, un cadeau de bienvenue ? Ils sont polis nos amis les « aliennes ». Oui, c'est ça qui a le plus de bon sens.

Mathilde Gauthier-Larocque, 11 ans, Beauport, QC
École Yves-Prévost

Je me suis toujours demandé pourquoi le ciel est bleu. Il serait
encore plus beau s'il était multicolore. Les nuages seraient beaux
s'ils étaient d'une autre couleur comme bleu, jaune, rouge, orange,
vert ou blanc. Si les nuages étaient tous différents : l'un serait
rouge, l'autre vert ou rouge et vert. Cela serait beaucoup plus
imaginaire ou fantaisiste. Il y aurait plus de personnes qui
regarderaient le ciel et les nuages. Quand il pleuverait, ça serait
de toutes les couleurs. Alors tout serait magnifique :
ciel, nuage et pluie.

Charles-Antoine Gélinas, 10 ans, St-Étienne-des-Grès, QC
École Amie-Joie

I've always wondered if there is such a place called Heaven. I've been told there is, but is there? I imagine Heaven would be magically beautiful, with lovely angels strolling on white, fluffy clouds. As their perfect wings take them to places we only dream about, flowers bloom and crystal clear water flows freely. When a loved one passes away, their soul has already departed. As they enter through God's Golden Gates, they gracefully turn into an angel. There is God, ever so welcoming, and yet solemn, for He has once again taken another from the mourning world below.

Lauren Gilbart   Age 12

I've always wondered if there is such a place called Heaven. I've been told there is, but is there? I imagine Heaven would be magically beautiful with lovely angels strolling on the white, fluffy clouds. As their perfect wings take them to places we only dream about, flowers bloom and crystal clear water flows freely. When a loved one passes away, their soul has already departed. As they enter through God's Golden Gates, they gracefully turn into an angel. There is God, ever so welcoming, and yet solemn, for he has once again taken another from the mourning world below.

Lauren Gilbart, Age 12, Calgary, AB
R.E. Osborne Junior High School

I've always wondered how everything (and I mean EVERYTHING!) started. Don't you ever wonder about that? Well, sometimes I wonder about it A LOT! How were all humans created? Who created them? Some say supernaturals created EVERYTHING, (even you and I). Is it true? I don't know, that's why I'm asking! Whenever I think about this question, I then think about how everything will, well... end. Boy, that question gives me the jitters! So, I will come to an "end" about that question. Get it? Never mind! How was everything started? I guess I'll never know (well, for _now_ anyway!).

THAMAYANTHI GIRITHARAN
AGE: 11

I've always wondered how everything (and I mean EVERYTHING!) started. Don't you every wonder about that? Well, sometimes I wonder about it A LOT. How were all humans created. Who created them? Some say supernaturals created EVERYTHING (even you and I). Is it true? I don't know, that's why I'm asking! Whenever I think about this question, I then think about how everything will, well... end. Boy, that question gives me the jitters! So, I'll come to an "end" about that question. Get it? Never mind! How was everything started? I guess I'll never know, (well, for now anyway!).

Thamayanthi Giritharan, Age 11, Toronto, ON
Valley Park M.S.

I've always wondered why blue skies always make me happy. It always makes me happy when I feel a soft wet puppy lick on my face, and watching his tail wagging. When I'm sad or mad I hug my teddy bears, they always make me feel better. When I get hurt my mom always takes care of me and gives me a hug. It always makes me happy knowing I helped someone in need. It always makes me happier to give rather than receive. It always makes me happy to see people smile.

Michelle Glavic ☺ Age 11

I've always wondered why blue skies always make me happy. It always makes me happy when I feel a soft wet puppy lick on my face, and watching his tail wagging. When I'm sad or mad I hug my teddy bears, they always make me feel better. When I get hurt my mom always takes care of me and gives me a hug. It always makes me happy knowing I helped someone in need. It always makes me happier to give rather than receive. It always makes me happy to see people smile.

Michelle Glavic, Age 11, Niagara Falls, ON
Prince Philip School

I've always wondered what it would be like to have a secret alien friend. One night I was alone in my room, when I thought I saw something fall out from heaven. I ran outside and was shocked to see a four-legged, three-eyed, two-foot tall creature that spoke English. He was friendly, so I let him in. Since then he was my best buddy, who was doing my homework, clearing my path from bullies and getting cobwebs out of my brain. I've always wondered what it would be like if all of the above wasn't a pigment of my imagination.

Martin Goodwein, Age 12, Oliver, BC
Oliver Elementary School

Je me suis toujours demandé comment les planètes naissent. Peut-être n'étaient-elles que de gros cailloux errant dans l'infini à la recherche d'une étoile chaleureuse à qui se confier ? Ou encore se sont-elles formées de milliards et de milliards de minuscules poussières attirées les unes vers les autres? Nul ne le sait, car il y a probablement plus d'explications plausibles que ce que l'imagination peut fournir. Chaque planète n'est peut-être qu'une poussière dans l'univers qui n'en est qu'un parmi tant d'autres ? C'est à croire qu'en chaque poussière il y a de quoi comparer l'univers. Je me suis toujours demandé ...

Vincent Goulet 12 ans

Je me suis toujours demandé comment les planètes naissent. Peut-être n'étaient-elles que de gros cailloux errant dans l'infini à la recherche d'une étoile chaleureuse à qui se confier ? Ou encore se sont-elles formées de milliards, de milliards de minuscules poussières attirées les unes vers les autres ? Nul ne le sait, il y a probablement plus d'explications plausibles que ce que l'imagination peut fournir. Chaque planète n'est peut-être qu'une poussière dans l'univers qui n'en est qu'un parmi tant d'autres ? C'est à croire qu'en chaque poussière il y a de quoi comparer l'univers? Je me suis toujours demandé…

Vincent Goulet, 12 ans, Ste-Marie de Beauce, QC
Polyvalente Benoît-Vachon

Je me suis toujours demandée ce que la fée des dents fait de toutes celles qu'elle accumule au fil du temps. La fée, petite ou grande, ailée ou non, les amasse mais dans quel but ? Peut-être veut-elle réaliser des milliers de colliers qu'elle répartira entre tous les enfants du monde ? Peut-être veut-elle bâtir un château digne d'un roi ? Peut-être est-elle maléfique ? Elle ramasse ces dents dans le seul but d'ensorceler ceux qui les lui ont offertes. Enfin, vous comprendrez que la fée des dents nous réserve bien des surprises...

Andréanne Gravel 10 ans

Je me suis toujours demandé ce que la fée des dents fait de toutes celles qu'elle accumule au fil du temps. La fée, petite ou grande, ailée ou non, les amasse mais dans quel but ? Peut-être veut-elle réaliser des milliers de colliers qu'elle répartira entre tous les enfants du monde ? Peut-être veut-elle bâtir un château digne d'un roi ? Peut-être est-elle maléfique ? Elle ramasse ces dents dans le seul but d'ensorceler ceux qui les lui ont offertes ? Enfin, vous comprendrez que la fée des dents nous réserve bien des surprises…

Andréanne Gravel, 10 ans, St-Bruno, QC
École de Montarville

I've always wondered why people give up their pets. Is it because they stink or is it because they bark when people come to the door? I don't know but I do know that it is wrong. I have a pet of my own and I would not ever think of giving her up. People should take care of their pets because when they're gone, people will regret it. I have a black lab at home and I would never ever give her up. I play with her every day and it will never stop.

Shannon Green, Age 9, Sisson Brook, NB
Donald Fraser Memorial

I've always wondered what it was like to fly and last night, I got my wish. I soared across the starry night sky, feeling excitement bubbling inside me. The moonlight glinted off my silky auburn wings as I flew over Barrie. The waters of Georgian Bay were still and mirrored the sky, making it seem like I was flying between worlds. I pumped my wings harder and flew higher, towards the clouds, with my strawberry blonde hair rippling in the wind. I reached out a timid hand and touched the clouds. Then my eyes opened. It was just a dream.

Emily Groh, age 12

I've always wondered what it was like to fly and last night, I got my wish. I soared across the starry night sky, feeling excitement bubbling inside me. The moonlight glinted off my silky auburn wings as I flew over Barrie. The waters of Georgian Bay were still and mirrored the sky, making it seem like I was flying between worlds. I pumped my wings harder and flew higher, towards the clouds, with my strawberry blond hair rippling in the wind. I reached out a timid hand and touched the clouds. Then my eyes opened. It was just a dream.

Emily Groh, Age 12, Barrie, ON
Oakley Park Public School

Je me suis toujours demandé si Max, mon petit frère serait venu d'ailleurs ! Par exemple, il enlève le crémage de ses biscuits Oréo et le remplace par une tranche de fromage. Il a les oreilles décollées et le nez retroussé. Un jour de pluie, Max est sorti de la maison avec sa salopette à pois. Soudain, une énorme soucoupe volante apparut au-dessus de sa tête. Une lumière verte sortit de la soucoupe et entraîna Max à l'intérieur. Une minute plus tard, Max en ressortit, mais avec une troupe de Martiens à pois. J'ai répondu à ma question !

Claudine Guérin, 10 ans, Longueuil, QC
École Armand-Racicot

I've always wondered what it would be like to be a pencil. It would be cool! You'd be able to make awesome pictures and the people that draw with you will go "Wow! How did I draw that!" If I were a pencil I'd wear a fancy pencil topper to look good, and show it off to my pencil friends. One of the best things about being a pencil would be that if you make a huge mistake you can always erase it. The only bad thing is at some POINT in time you'd have to be sharpened! Ouch!

Sierra Guindon, 9

I've always wondered what it would be like to be a pencil. It would be cool! You'd be able to make awesome pictures and the people that draw with you will go "Wow! How did I draw that?" If I were a pencil I'd wear a fancy pencil topper to look good, and show it off to my pencil friends. One of the best things about being a pencil would be that if you make a huge mistake you can always erase it. The only bad thing is at some POINT in time, you'd have to be sharpened! Ouch!

Sierra Guindon, Age 9, Belleville, ON
Our Lady of Fatima

90

I've always wondered how grocery items feel about being moved around so much. First we take them off the shelves and put them in the cart. Then we put them on the check-out counter. After that, we load them back in the cart all squished together with other food. Imagine how scared they are! Then we load them in our cars and drive home. Then we take the terrified groceries out of the car, and put them where they belong in the kitchen. No wonder you can never find exactly what you need, the groceries are hiding from us!

Caroline Hanson, 11

I've always wondered how grocery items feel about being moved around so much. First we take them off the shelves and put them in the cart. Then we put them on the check-out counter. After that we load them back in the cart all squished together with other food. Imagine how scared they are! Then we load them in our cars and drive home. Then we take the terrified groceries out of the car, and put them where they belong in the kitchen. No wonder you can never find exactly what you need, the groceries are hiding from us!

Caroline Hanson, Age 11, Fort McMurray, AB
St. Gabriel School

I've always wondered what happens inside the paper mill. I'm a tree and I've been here for fifteen years. Every day I hear a chainsaw and see trees falling down. One day I heard a chainsaw; I was falling; being carried away. My bark was stripped. I didn't think I wanted to know what happens inside a papermill anymore! But then I came out as a sheet of paper that was sold to a girl. She used me to write a story and enter it in a contest. She won the top prize from her favourite store, STAPLES!

Rachel Harris, 10

I've always wondered what happens inside the paper mill. I'm a tree and I've been here for fifteen years. Every day I hear a chainsaw and see trees falling down. One day I heard a chainsaw; I was falling; being carried away. My bark was stripped. I didn't think I wanted to know what happens inside a paper mill anymore! But then I came out as a sheet of paper that was sold to a girl. She used me to write a story and enter it in a contest. She won the top prize from her favourite store, STAPLES!

Rachel Harris, Age 10, St. John's, NL
Vanier Elementary School

I've always wondered if dogs come from a different planet. Why you may ask? Really, a shooting star is not what you think it is. According to me a shooting star is a dog's spaceship. When you see a wolf howling at the moon it means he is homesick because the moon represents his home. Why do dogs come to our planet you may ask? Dogs come to our planet because they're sent by the queen dog to keep the children happy. Once every year the queen dog comes to earth for inspection. If they don't pass they go home.

Eric Harvey, 10 years old

I've always wondered if dogs come from a different planet. Why you may ask? Really, a shooting star is not what you think it is. According to me a shooting star is a dog's spaceship. When you see a wolf howling at the moon it means he is homesick because the moon represents his home. Why do dogs come to our planet you may ask? Dogs come to our planet because they're sent by the queen dog to keep the children happy. Once every year the queen dog comes to earth for inspection. If they don't pass, they go home.

Eric Harvey, Age 10, Montreal, QC
United Talmud Torah

I've always wondered what it would be like to be a hockey puck. He shoots, He scores I hit the back of the net. I love the sound of the crowd, the pride of scoring and the sense of being part of the game. I chip but I do not break as I hit the boards. As a player shoots me I hit the goalies stick and fly over the glass and into a childs hand. After the game I get autographed. It is ticklish as the marker rubs against me and the child cares and cherishes me forever and ever.

Brendan Hastie 11 yrs

I've always wondered what it would be like to be a hockey puck. He shoots, he scores, I hit the back of the net. I love the sound of the crowd, the pride of scoring and the sense of being part of the game. I chip but do not break as I hit the boards. As a player shoots me, I hit the goalie's stick and fly over the glass and into a child's hand. After the game, I get autographed. It is ticklish as the marker rubs against me and the child cares and cherishes me forever and ever.

Brendan Hastie, Age 11, St. Catherines, ON
St. Christopher School

I've always wondered what it's like to fly; to soar high, through the clouds; to sail across the vast, blue sky and feel the cold, powerful wind brush against my cheeks, freshening up my exhausted mind. I wonder what it's like to have the wing of an eagle, strong and mighty to carry me through the atmosphere, floating up above the world. Maybe I'll fly up to the moon and just sit among millions of stars in the Milky-Way, observing the exotic view of our beautiful mother Earth from outer-space, while enjoying the magic as this dream works its wonders.

Sophia He, 12

I've always wondered what it's like to fly, to soar high, through the clouds, to sail across the vast, blue sky and feel the cold, powerful wind brush against my cheeks, freshening up my exhausted mind. I wonder what it's like to have the wing of an eagle, strong and mighty to carry me through the atmosphere, floating up above the world. Maybe I'll fly up to the moon and just sit among millions of stars in the Milky-Way, observing the exotic view of our beautiful Mother Earth from outer-space, while enjoying the magic as this dream work its wonders.

Sophia He, Age 12, Richmond Hill, ON
H.G. Bernard

I've always wondered why books can't read themselves. But if books did, it would be strange. Once upon a time there was a girl who hated reading. One night, as she was reading, wishing her book would read itself, the book started to read. "Ahh," she shrieked. "Is everything okay Emily?" Emily's mother called. "Everything's fine," she replied. Her book continued to read. When it was time for bed, Emily had to bury her book in toys so that she could sleep. Her book wouldn't stop reading! So never wish your book will read itself, because it might not stop.

Ainsleigh Hill, Age 8

I've always wondered why books can't read themselves. But if books did, it would be strange… Once upon a time there was a girl who hated reading. One night, as she was reading, wishing her book would read itself, the book started to read. "Ahh," she shrieked. "Is everything okay Emily?" Emily's mother called. "Everything's fine," she replied. Her book continued to read. When it was time for bed, Emily had to bury her book in toys so that she could sleep. Her book wouldn't stop reading! So never wish your book will read itself, because it might not stop.

Ainsleigh Hill, Age 8, Victoria, BC
Pacific Christian School

I've always wondered why everyone is different colours and why can't we all be the same colours? But if we all were the same colour it would be boring to see the same colour everyday. Why can't we all be rich and live in mansoins and have millons of dollars? It don't matter what colour you are or what you look like as long as your nice in the inside. Colour don't matter you could be pink or green it's no different then anyone else. You can have hair or no hair everyone is speical in there own way too!

Alana Hogg age 13

I've always wondered why everyone is different colours and why can't we all be the same colours? But if we all were the same colour it would be boring to see the same colour every day. Why can't we all be rich and live in mansions and have millions of dollars? It doesn't matter what colour you are or what you look like as long as you're nice in the inside. Colour doesn't matter you could be pink or green it's no different then anyone else. You can have hair or no hair. Everyone is special in their own way too!

Alana Hogg, Age 13, Shelburne County, NS
Forest Ridge Academy

I've always wondered if dragons actually ever roamed the world. There are many myths and legends about these medieval creatures, but nobody can prove that dragons really ever lived thousands of years ago. Most people believe dragons were huge, scaly, fire breathing serpents with sharp claws and gigantic wings that guarded medieval treasures, destroyed towns and represented evil. In medieval tales, knights would slay dragons, save princesses and become great heroes. Many knights attempted this heroic feat, but few actually succeeded. Nobody knows for sure that dragons really ever existed outside of our imaginations. Will it remain a mystery forever?

Jillien Hone, 11 yrs old

I've always wondered if dragons actually ever roamed the world. There are many myths and legends about these medieval creatures, but nobody can prove that dragons really ever lived thousands of years ago. Most people believe dragons were huge, scaly, fire breathing serpents with sharp claws  and gigantic wings that guarded medieval treasures, destroyed towns and represented evil. In medieval tales, knights would slay dragons, save princesses and become great heroes. Many knights attempted this heroic feat, but few actually succeeded. Nobody knows for sure that dragons really ever existed outside of our imaginations. Will it remain a mystery forever?

Jillien Hone, Age 11, Port Hope, ON
Central Public School

I've always wondered what it would be like to visit Onionville I'm Ziblett I work for Pesky Problems My boss Colonel Shoeball assigned me to solve the case of the Rotting Onions. Everything is Rotting in Onionville. I Zoomed to onionville. I didn't cry from the smell of onions! I saw the planet Suferdudesville come really fast toward Onionville. Water from the planet splashed Onionville turning it into onion mush. I lassoed it between Fishyville and Unwetville, two planets that wouldn't be hurt by water. In no time Onionville started to smell again! The people cried and cried.

Jenna Horback   age 9

I've always wondered what it would be like to visit Onionville. I'm Ziblett. I work for Pesky Problems. My boss Colonel Shoeball assigned me to solve the case of the rotting onions. Everything is rotting in Onionville. I zoomed to Onionville. I didn't cry from the smell of onions! I saw the planet Suferdudesville come really fast toward Onionville. Water from the planet splashed Onionville turning it into onion mush. I lassoed it between Fishyville and Unwetville, two planets that wouldn't be hurt by water. In no time, Onionville started to smell again! The people cried and cried.

Jenna Horback, Age 9, Calgary, AB
School of Hope

I've always wondered what I will be when I grow up. I thought of some things like being a teacher, an artist or a composer. I don't know how I'm going to decide. But who knows it might just pop into my mind someday, that I definitely might be one of the things I named. I play school with my sister, so I just might be a teacher. I am really good at drawing, so maybe I will be an artist. I like to play the piano, so I might be a composer. Soon I'll have to decide.

Rachel Hudson, 9

I've always wondered what I will be when I grow up. I thought of some things like being a teacher, an artist or a composer. I don't know how I'm going to decide. But who knows it might just pop into my mind someday, that I definitely might be one of the things I named. I play school with my sister, so I just might be a teacher. I am really good at drawing, so maybe I will be an artist. I like to play the piano, so I might be a composer. Soon I'll have to decide.

Rachel Hudson, Age 9, Lower Coverdale, NB
Gunningsville School

I've always wondered: is there a monster under my bed? While below a monster wonders in fear: is there really a human up there? The boy's mother comforts, "Don't be silly dear. Of course there isn't a monster down there!" Little do they know, that below them still the monster's mom says, "There's no human up there!"

"But will you check?" ask the boy and the monster. "That's your job, my dear." answer their mothers. "Good night" they say, and switch off the light. The two creep to each others' beds, and find with relief, there is no one there.

Amelia Hunter, age 10

I've always wondered is there a monster under my bed? While below a monster wonders in fear: is there really a human up there? The boy's mother comforts, "Don't be silly dear. Of course there isn't a monster down there!" Little do they know, that below them still, the monster's mom says "There's no humans up there." "But will you check?" ask the boy and the monster "That's your job, my dear," answer their mothers. "Good night," they say and switch off the light. The two creep to each other's beds and find with relief there is no one there.

Amelia Hunter, Age 10, London, ON
St. Thomas Moore Elementary

I've always wondered what happens to your reflection in a puddle when you walk away. One day, I decided to find out myself. It had rained abundantly the night before, so I sloshed over to a calm puddle. My smiling reflection stared back. Suddenly, the world flipped upside down. I'm a reflection! If the real me leaves, I'm trapped! Desperately, I touched the puddle floating lonely above me. My hand slipped through! All I'll have to do is jump up and I'll be in the real world! I succeeded, but nothing will ever be scarier than being trapped in a puddle.

Peggy Jankovic, Age 12, Edmonton, AB
École Holly Cross School

"I've always wondered", said a fish. "What do bananas taste like?" "I do not know" said his friend. "Let's ask the whale." So the fish went to see the whale. "Do you know what bananas taste like?" the fish asked the whale. "I do not know, but I know some dolphins that do" the whale answered. So the fish asked the dolphins. "Do you know what bananas taste like?" "Yes" said the dolphins. They jumped up and got the fish a banana. "We like bananas!" said the fish. "We do too" said the dolphins. So they ate bananas together.

Taylor Jarvis

"I've always wondered," said a fish, "What do bananas taste like?" "I do not know," said his friend, "Let's go ask the whale." So the fish went to see the whale. "Do you know what bananas taste like?" the fish asked the whale. "I do not know, but I know some dolphins that do," the whale answered. So the fish asked the dolphins, "Do you know what bananas taste like?" "Yes," said the dolphins. They jumped up and got the fish a banana. "We like bananas!" said the fish. "We do too," said the dolphins. So they ate bananas together.

Taylor Jarvis, Age 9, Black Creek, BC
Miracle Beach Elementary

I've always wondered if nature can communicate like you and me. Plants and animals can eat and breathe like people. But why can't they communicate like people? Is it possible? I often stare at plants for quite a while, and try to pick up on their conversations. When I peek at animals, I hear them bark and chirp, and all their other weird noises. But is that really their own language? How can they understand each other when everything they say sounds the same. "Woof, woof, woof!" And "chirp, chirp, chirp!" Can this really be? It's what I've always wondered.

Yaanu Jeyakumar Age: 7

I've always wondered if nature can communicate like you and me. Plants and animals can eat and breathe like people. But why can't they communicate like people? Is it possible? I often stare at plants for quite a while, and try to pick up on their conversations. When I peek at animals, I hear them bark and chirp, and all their other weird noises. But is that really their own language? How can they understand each other when everything, they say, sounds the same. "Woof, woof, woof!" And "chirp, chirp, chirp!" Can this really be? It's what I've always wondered.

Yaanu Jeyakumar, Age 7, Toronto, ON
Ionview Public School

I've always wondered if chickens ate crayons? Maybe there is no Easter bunny, but an Easter chicken. What if some specail chickens live in a Crayola Factory. They Would need to eat a lot of crayons to supply the world with beautifull colored Easter eggs. I also don't know of any rabbits any where that have ever layed an egg! So even if rabbits are responible for delivering the eggs at Easter, they still would have to get them from the chickens. I'm still wondering if the chickens make the designs on the Easter eggs; but thats another story. Bye.

Megan Jurczak   age 7

I've always wondered if chickens eat crayons? Maybe there is no Easter bunny, but an Easter chicken. What if some special chickens live in a crayola factory? They would need to eat a lot of crayons to supply the world with beautiful coloured Easter eggs. I also don't know of any rabbits anywhere that have ever laid an egg! So even if the rabbits are responsible for delivering the eggs at Easter, they still would have to get them from the chickens. I'm still wondering if the chickens make the designs on the Easter eggs, but that's another story. Bye.

Megan Jurczak, Age 7, Calgary, AB
Father James Whelihan School

I've always wondered about the riddle "Hey Diddle Diddle." Like come on!! The cat playing the fiddle! I can't even play the fiddle; how can a cat play a fiddle?

Imagine a dog laughing - bow wow wow woof ha ha grrr.

When the dish ran away with the spoon, I'm guessing the spoon was married.

The cow must have been huge because it was seen all the way from earth. That's one big cow! Too bad it wasn't a pig because when I want something expensive my mom says "When pigs fly!"

Emerald Kains 11 yrs old

I've always wondered about the riddle "Hey diddle diddle." Like come on! The cat playing the fiddle! I can't even play fiddle; how can a cat play a fiddle? Imagine a dog laughing – bow wow wow woof ha ha grrr. When the dish ran away with the spoon. I'm guessing the spoon was married. The cow must have been huge because it was seen all the way from earth. That's one big cow! Too bad it wasn't a pig because when I want something expensive my mom says "when pigs fly!"

Emerald Kains, Age 11, Whitehorse, YK
Takhini Elementary School

I've always wondered about being rich. Rich clothings, expensive school, admiration and most of all, a big mansion with five floors and tons of servants. Then there will be indoor pools plus ten balconies, escalators, expensive furnitures and billions more. Oh, how wonderful! Guess what? My dream had already come true. My father won a one hundred million lottery for first prize. My mom won a one hundred thousand lottery for second prize. So now, I'm wearing a hand made velvet skirt at Riches Private School writing my story. How do you like to be moi!

Noelle Kan, 9

I've always wondered about being rich. Rich clothings, expensive school, admiration and most of all, a big mansion with five floors and tons of servants. Then there will be indoor pools plus ten balconies, escalators, expensive furnitures and billions more. Oh, how wonderful! Guess what? My dream had already came true. My father won a one hundred million lottery for first prize. My mom won a one hundred thousand lottery for second prize. So now, I'm wearing a hand made velvet skirt at Riches Private School writing my story. How do you like to be moi!

Noelle Kan, Age 9, North York, ON
Finch P.S.

I've always wondered if there are unicorns in the sky. Flutter, floating, flying, passing beautifully by. I've always wondered, are there castles up there? I wonder, do unicorns have nice, beautiful hair? What about candy, balloons, popcorn ho boy. Think of all the stuff unicorns have up there...oy! While I'm in school, I dream about owning a unicorn. After school, I'd prance and play, comb her mane and shine her horn. Please, I can't wait get me a unicorn for my next birthday. I'll feed her I promise, just find me some hay.
Or should I get a pony?

Kelly Kanhoffen age 11

I've always wondered if there are unicorns in the sky. Flutter, floating, flying, passing beautifully by. I've always wondered, are there castles up there? I wonder, do unicorns have nice, beautiful hair? What about candy, balloons, popcorn, oh  boy! Think of all the stuff unicorns have up there… oy! While I'm in school, I dream about owning a unicorn. After school, I'd prance and play, comb her mane and shine her horn. Please, I can't wait to get me a unicorn for my next birthday. I'll feed her I promise, just get me some hay. Or should I get a pony?

Kelly Kanhoffen, Age 11, Victoria, BC
Wishart School

I've always wondered whether stuffed animals are real. Maybe they can talk, maybe not. Our story begins long ago back when dragons soared the sky, there lived a little girl named Sally. She was curious and had love for adventure. One day she found a door in the attic. It was stuck. Her mom's voice echoed in her head. "Don't open any doors in the attic." Sally laughed and pushed again. It opened. She gasped. There were tons of stuffed animals. She picked one up, and to her surprise it said "Hey" Sally screamed and never opened the door again.

By: Harini Kav Age: 10

I've always wondered whether stuffed animals are real. Maybe they can talk, maybe not. Our story begins long ago back when dragons soared the sky, there lived a little girl, named Sally. She was curious and had love for adventure. One day she found a door in the attic. It was stuck. Her mom's voice echoed in her head "don't open any doors in the attic." Sally laughed and pushed again. It opened. She gasped. There were tons of stuffed animals. She picked one up and to her surprise it said "Hey!" Sally screamed and never opened that door again.

Harini Kav, Age 10, Edmonton, AB
Julia Kiniski P.S.

I've always wondered how things can be so big like the ocean when you're a tiny boat and the sky if you're a little bird; a body so big when you are a cell and the world so big when you are a child. I've always wondered how a garden can be so big when you are a bug, a tree be so big when you're a new green leaf, a universe so big when you are a spaceship or a beach so big when you're a grain of sand. I've always wondered am I big or am I small?

Sarah Kember, 10

I've always wondered how things can be so big, like the ocean when you're a tiny boat and the sky if you're a little bird, a body so big when you are a cell and the world so big when you are a child. I've always wondered how a garden can be so big when you are a bug, a tree be so big when you're a new green leaf, a universe so big when you are a spaceship or a beach so big when you're a grain of sand. I've always wondered, am I big or am I small?

Sarah Kember, Age 10, Summerside, PEI
Athena Consolidated School

I've always wondered if I could get rid of the ugly troll who lived under my bed. When it was night I had to be careful because I didn't want to wake him. I thought of a smart idea. I went to the kitchen and brought peas, cookies, and peanut butter. I put peas next to my bed, cookies in the living room, and peanut butter in front house. No longer the troll came out to eat. He ate peas, then I followeed him to front door. I slammed the door and locked it. I went back to bed and slept.

Carol Khoury, 8 years old

I've always wondered if I could get rid of the ugly troll who lived under my bed. When it was night I had to be careful because I didn't want to wake him. I thought of a smart idea. I went to the kitchen and brought peas, cookies and peanut butter. I put peas next to my bed, cookies in the living room, and peanut butter in the front house. No longer the troll came out to eat. He ate peas, then I followed him to the front door. I slammed the door and locked it. I went back to bed and slept.

Carol Khoury, Age 8, Toronto, ON
Our Lady of the Assumption

I've always wondered what life would be like for a Canadian flag. Imagine if a Canadian flag could say one sentence about it's life, what would it be? Would it love the windy days, whipping back and forth as if on a rollercoaster? Would it admire the way Canadians stand proud while singing the national anthem? Would it be boasting about what it represents, freedom, honor, and justice? I can just imagine the twinkle in it's eye and it's smile reaching ear to ear when it thinks about it's life. I imagine that it would have a very good life.

Andrea Klein : age 12

I've always wondered what life would be like for a Canadian Flag. Imagine if a Canadian Flag could say one sentence about its life, what would it be? Would it love the windy days, whipping back and forth as if on a rollercoaster? Would it admire the way Canadians stand proud while singing the national anthem? Would it be boasting about what it represents, freedom, honour and justice? I can just imagine the twinkle in its eye and its smile reaching ear to ear when it thinks about its life.I imagine that it would have a very good life.

Andrea Klein, Age 12, Kitchener, ON
Laurentian Hills Christian School

I've always wondered if I was adopted. My mom, of course, says no, but I must be. I'm not related to them, they're different from me. I have four legs, but they have two. We all have curly hair, but theirs is only on their heads. They have a complex language while I can only bark. I eat from a bowl placed on the floor and they have a grand table, but that doesn't matter. I never did mind the leash, plus I love them and they love me.

Hannah Koke, 11

I've always wondered if I was adopted. My mom, of course, says no, but I must be. I'm not related to them, they're different from me. I have four legs but they have two. We all have curly hair, but theirs is only on their heads. They have a complex language while I can only bark. I eat from a bowl placed on the floor and they get a grand table, but that doesn't matter. I never did mind the leash, plus I love them and they love me.

Hannah Koke, Age 11, Pickering, ON
Frenchman's Bay Public School

I've always wondered why dogs have fur. My mom says without fur dogs would be cold in the winter. My dad says it would be better if they didn't have fur so they wouldn't shed so much. My sister says they wouldn't be so cuddly without fur. My brother says they would be too pinkish like a girl. I thought and thought and it hit me. If dogs didn't have fur they would look too much like pigs and if they looked like pigs there would be no such thing as dogs. So now I see why dogs have fur.

Bethany Konink 11yrs

I've always wondered why dogs have fur. My mom says without fur dogs would be cold in the winter. My dad says it would be better if they didn't have fur so they wouldn't shed so much. My sister says they wouldn't be so cuddly without fur. My brother says they would be too pinkish like girls. I thought and thought and it hit me. If dogs didn't have fur they would look too much like pigs and if they looked like pigs there would be no such things as dogs. So now I see why dogs have fur.

Bethany Konink, Age 11, Cornwall, ON
Rothwell-Osnabruck P.S.

"I've always wondered what it would be like to have a home," thought Mary the porcelain doll. Mary sighed. "I guess I'll never know." Meanwhile, six year old Rebecca was walking down the aisle looking at the toys when she noticed Mary. Mary was the last of the dolls. "Oh look mom!" exclaimed Rebecca. "Would you like to have that doll?" offered Rebecca's mother. "OH YES PLEASE!" Rebecca said excitedly. Mary had curly, blonde hair and a blue dress. Rebecca looked deeply into Mary's dark blue eyes. They both knew this would be the beginning of a beautiful friendship.

Amber Krogel, Age 10, Kelowna, BC
Kelowna Christian School

I've always wondered what kind of pajamas principals wear. Do they wear silky blue ones? Or frilly pink ones? Or baseball ones? Or even lime green ones with lavender spots! Maybe they have plain white ones, and when we do something bad, and get sent down to the principal's office, the principal will go home, whip out a black, permanent marker, and write our names on his pajamas. Maybe that's how the principal remembers us bad kids so well!

Holly Kwok, 11

I've always wondered what kind of pajamas principals wear at night. Do they wear silky blue ones? Or frilly pink ones? Or baseball ones? Or even lime green ones with lavendar spots! Maybe they have plain white ones and when we do something bad, and get sent down to the principal's office, the principal will go home, whip out a black, permanent marker and write our names down on his pajamas. Maybe that's how the principal remembers us bad kids so well!

Holly Kwok, Age 11, Scarborough, ON
Churchill Heights P.S.

I've always wondered how it feels to have the wind at your back. Racing unknown trails. Soaring on the back of a stallon. Colors of autumn fall around me. Sparkling powder surrounds me, twinkling like summer water. Looking out into the hazy blue, all fog as we run. Wind in our hair as we soar. Every leaf that touches the ground, everything that makes a sound, comes to our ears. The world around us is still. Only us. Frozen in time, we ride through the clouds, over obstacles great and small.
This is the Life for me.

Kaitlyn Laaper   age .12.

I've always wondered how it feels to have the wind at your back. Racing unknown trails. Soaring on the back of a stallion. Colours of autumn fall around me. Sparkling powder surrounds me, twinkling like the summer water. Looking out into the hazy blue, all fog as we run. Wind in our hair as we soar. Every leaf that touches the ground, everything that makes a sound, comes to our ears. The world around us is still. Only us. Frozen in time, we ride through the clouds, over obstacles great and small. This is the life for me.

Kaitlyn Laaper, Age 12, Saint John, NB
Hampton Middle School

I've always wondered if unicorns were real. Until one night, when I was lying in bed, I heard a queer noise outside. I was curious and went to investigate. I quickly put on my robe and tiptoed quietly down the steps and outside. It was totally dark, I couldn't see where I was going. Suddenly, I bumped into something which felt very soft. I felt around to it's head. That's when I noticed a beautiful blue light shining infront of me. I just stood and stared. The light belonged to the most marvelous creature called the unicorn!

Olivia Leblanc   Age: 7

I've always wondered if unicorns were real. Until one night, when I was lying in bed, I heard a queer noise outside. I was curious and went to investigate. I quickly put on my robe and tiptoed quietly down the steps and outside. It was totally dark, I couldn't see where I was going. Suddenly, I bumped into something which felt very soft. I felt around to its head. That's when I noticed a beautiful blue light shining in front of me. I just stood and stared. The light belonged to the most marvelous creature called the unicorn!

Olivia Leblanc, Age 7, Prospect Bay, NB
Atlantic Memorial School

Je me suis toujours demandé pourquoi les vaches ont des taches.
Peut-être qu'elles se sont roulées dans la boue ou que c'est à
cause d'une maladie rare ? Mais pourquoi pas des taches
vertes ? Ça serait bien plus à la mode ! En plus d'être drôle,
ça déguiserait les vaches pour l'Halloween ! Je pense qu'avant
elles avaient des taches vertes jusqu'au jour de l'Halloween.
Tout le monde avait sans doute trop peur ! Mais de toute façon,
si les vaches avaient des taches vertes, j'imagine qu'on aurait
du lait vert ! Est-ce que vous en boiriez ?

Guillaume L'Écuyer, 10 ans, St-Élie-d'Orford, QC
École Alfred-DesRochers

Je me suis toujours demandé si un jour j'allais grandir.
Je suis tellement petite qu'il faut baisser la tête pour me voir.
Un jour j'ai demandé à ma mère, « Maman, est-ce qu'un jour
je grandirai ? » Elle m'a répondu, « Tu sais Marie, dans la vie
nous ne sommes pas faits pour être parfaits. Ce n'est pas
l'extérieur qui compte, mais l'intérieur. » Alors j'ai compris !
Je suis petite d'extérieur mais grande d'intérieur. Alors si je sors
de mon trou et que je prouve que j'existe, j'en arriverais à bout !
Les gens me remarqueront enfin ! Alors c'est ça prouvez-le et
EXISTEZ !

Daphné Lefebvre, 10 ans, St-Jérôme, QC
École La Fourmilière

Je me suis toujours demandé où allaient les trous que nous faisions dans nos vêtements ? Or, un certain soir j'arrivai devant un château. J'approchai lentement et vis par la fenêtre des princesses couturières. Leur corps était en forme d'aiguille, leur nez en dé à coudre, leurs mains en ficelle, leurs yeux en boutons multicolores. Le roi et la reine, tous deux machines à coudre, s'amusaient à réparer les vêtements à gros trous. Puis, la musique commença et les princes en forme de fermeture éclair vinrent chercher leur belle amoureuse. Mon réveille-matin sonne. Mon très beau rêve était maintenant terminé.

Alessia-Rose Legault, 9 ans, Gatineau, QC
École des Trois-Saisons

I've always wondered what it would be like in Candyland. There would be cinnamon heart trees that have mint leaves and chocolate trunks. The flowers would be made of icing with a cotton candy sky and marshmallow clouds. The apple pie sun with red licorice sun beams would shine down on the Koolaid lake. The houses made of wafer cookies and roofs made of gumdrops filled with Sour Patch families. The pet would be a gummy bear. Taffy bar cars drive on the glass candy roads surrounded by green sugar grass. Then, I wake up from my sweet dream.

Kaitlyn Legge, Age 10, Cambridge, ON
St. Brigid

I've always wondered how the fruits and the vegetables ripen. At the beginning, the vegetables are green and when they ripen, they become red. How? I think that it's garden dwarves. Yes! They paint the tomato with a special painting. Every day the garden dwarves paint the vegetables one shade darker. They do this for each fruit and vegetable. At the end, the tomato is ripe and ready for my lunch. Now we know the secret of "how fruits and vegetables ripen!"

Théo Lessard, 12 years old

I've always wondered how the fruits and the vegetables ripen. At the beginning the vegetables are green and when they ripen they become red. How? I think that it's garden dwarves. Yes! They paint the tomato with a special painting. Every day the garden dwarves paint the vegetables one shade darker. They do this for each fruit and vegetable. At the end, the tomato is ripe and ready for my lunch. Now, we know the secret of "how fruits and vegetables ripen!"

Théo Lessard, Age 12, Montreal, QC
Sophie Barat High School

Je me suis toujours demandé : comment ce serait d'avoir des ailes et être un oiseau ? Si j'avais des ailes, je ne marcherais plus. Seulement dans la maison, je ralentirais et je marcherais. Mais si je voulais aller à une autre ville, je ne prendrais pas l'avion, ni le train mais je volerais ! Ça serait gratuit. Mais si j'étais fatigué de voler ? Je ne pourrais pas prendre l'avion parce que je serais considéré « animal ». Peut-être tout le monde serait des humains-ailés ! Les avions seraient des machines pour les fatigués ! Si j'avais des ailes, à mon avis ça serait merveilleux !

Malcolm Lewis-Richmond, 10 ans, Montréal, QC
École Willingdon

I've always wondered where you go, Wind, after you caress each leaf of my poplar tree and waltz a twig gently to the earth. I've always wondered how you build your nest, Little Bird, with such perfection. Lifting that twig from the earth, you carry it to your task. How does your beak become a pair of knitting needles weaving and bending each twig into perfect place? Then, how can you leave your nest one day as if no work was put into it at all, leaving only tiny feathers of babies gone to be carried away by Wind?

Olivia Loccisano age: 11

I've always wondered where you go, Wind, after you caress each leaf of my poplar tree and waltz a twig gently to the earth. I've always wondered how you build your nest, Little Bird, with such perfection. Lifting that twig from the earth, you carry it to your task. How does your beak become a pair of knitting needles weaving and bending each twig into perfect place? Then, how can you leave your nest one day as if no work was put into it at all, leaving only tiny feathers of babies gone to be carried away by Wind?

Olivia Loccisano, Age 11, Etobicoke, ON
St. Patrick School

"I've always wondered" what the world would be like if there was no killing, fighting or hunger. Only if there was nothing but love amongst the human being. I think if we all tried a little harder, we can achieve peace. Insted of hurting other people, we should try to work things out. We should all think of the less fortunate people and share our love, give what we can so they do not die of hunger, sickness because they do not have money or resources. If we all tried we can do it. We will have a perfect world!

Karen Luddu   Age: 8

I've always wondered what the world be like if there was no killing, fighting or hunger. Only if there was nothing but love amongst all the human being. I think if we all tried a little harder, we can achieve peace. Instead of hurting other people we should try to work things out. We should all think of the less fortunate people and share our love, give what we can so they do not die of hunger, sickness because they do not have money or resources. If we all tried we can do it. We will have a perfect world.

Karen Luddu, Age 8, Vancouver, BC
Pierre Elliott Trudeau Elementary

I've always wondered...
if animals have their own worlds.
We can't be the only ones who
have cities and towns. Do cats have
scratching post cities? Do bears have
honeypot homes? Do dogs have hard bone
floors? Maybe these animal cities are
called: Catontsia? Dogmonton? Mousehole
park? Humans can't be the only ones.
Maybe they build them deep underground,
So we can't find them. Maybe they
put them in abandoned buildings,
So we won't look there. Or maybe
they put magical spells on their places,
So they are invisible. We can't be the
only ones with our own towns and
cities

Allison Mackay age 9

I've always wondered if animals have their own worlds. We
can't be the only ones who have cities and towns. Do cats have
scratching post cities? Do bears have honey pot homes? Do dogs
have hard bone floors? Maybe these animal cities are called:
Catonisia? Dogmonton? Mousehold Park? Humans can't be
the only ones. Maybe they build them deep underground, so
we can't find them. Maybe they put them in abandoned buildings
so we won't look there. Or maybe they put magical spells on
their places, so they are invisible. We can't be the only ones
with our own towns and cities.

Allison Mackay, Age 9, Bawlf, AB
Bawlf School

I've always wondered what it would be like if I was the Earth. To pass the time, I would look at the stars. I would have a job to turn around and turn around the sun. I would be able to see what is beyond the universe. The Earth's core is my heart and each layer of dirt is my body. The trees and plants are my hair and flowers are my perfume. The oceans and the rain are my blood. If I was the Earth I would always wonder what it would be like, if I was human.

Theron Maggs 11 yrs

I've always wondered what it would be like if I was the Earth.
To pass the time, I would look at the stars. I would have a job to
turn around and turn around the sun. I would be able to see what
is beyond the universe. The Earth's core is my heart and each
layer of dirt is my body. The trees and plants are my hair and
flowers are my perfume. The oceans and the rain are my blood.
If I was the Earth I would always wonder what it would be like,
if I was human.

Theron Maggs, Age 11, Welland, ON
St-François

I've always wondered if there are other life forms out there. Do they have their own world and cities? If they are there do you think they wonder about us and if there are other life forms, besides them? What if they have already found us, will they destroy us or take over our planet? They might disguise themselves to look like people. Maybe some are already on Earth hiding where people can't see them. Are they small or are they huge monsters? Are they near or are they far away? Are they coming or are they leaving? Who knows?

Jordan Magnuson Age: 12

I've always wondered if there are other life forms out there. Do they have their own world and cities? If they are there do you think they wonder about us and if there are other life forms, besides them? What if they have already found us, will they destroy us or take over our planet? They might disguise themselves to look like people. Maybe some are already on Earth hiding where people can't see them. Are they small or are they huge monsters? Are they near or are they far away? Are they coming or are they leaving? Who knows?

Jordan Magnuson, Age 12, Williams Lake, BC
Kwaleen Traditional Elementary

I've always wondered what it would be like If I were three inches tall. If I was, I would go swimming in my sink, to me the sink would be the size of a swimming pool. That would be fun! I would also drive in a remote control car. I would drive around the house. My dog would be the size of an elephant to me. I would ride on his back and we would charge around the yard. I would have lots of fun if I were three inches tall!

Aden Mah age 9

I've always wondered what it would be like if I was three inches tall. If I was, I would go swimming in my sink, to me the sink would be the size of a swimming pool. That would be fun! I would also drive in a remote control car. I would drive around the house. My dog would be the size of an elephant to me. I would ride on his back and we would charge around the yard. I would have a lot of fun if I was three inches tall!

Aden Mah, Age 9, Saskatoon, SK
École River Heights School

I've always wondered why boxing rings are square? Clearly
a ring is a circle, yet wrestlers fight on a square pad. So should
they not call it a boxing square? Just like the expressions our
noses run and our feet smell! How could our noses go anywhere
when they're attached to our faces? And our feet can definitely
not smell but they can sure run. So many people say these
phrases each day but does anyone notice this odd wording?
Like why do ships carry cargoes and cars carry shipments.
I've always wondered these things, have you?

Tanis Makowsky, Age 12, Nanoose Bay, BC
Springwood Middle School

Je me suis toujours demandé comment les volcans se mettent
en éruption. J'ai couru à mon ordinateur pour aller sur un site
internet. J'ai appris que le plus grand volcan d'Europe en activité
est l'Etna. Ensuite, je suis allé cliquer à quelque part dans mon
ordinateur mais il ne fallait pas que je clique là. Alors il s'est
éteint ! Quand ma maman a vu ça, sa figure est devenue rouge,
le feu lui sortait par les oreilles. Maintenant, je sais comment
les volcans se mettent en éruption ! Ils se fâchent !

Edouard Maltais, 9 ans, St-Nicéphore, QC
École St-Nicéphore

Je me suis toujours demandé pourquoi la faim existe encore dans le monde. Ça me rend triste de savoir que d'autres enfants n'ont pas de nourriture. Alors j'ai posé la question à une petite souris que je connais. Elle m'a dit que si chacun partageait ce qu'il possède, plus personne n'aurait faim la petite souris a rajouté que chacun a quelque chose a donner. Si on n'a pas d'argent on a au moins un sourire à partager. Un sourire ne coût rien mais il peut réchauffer un coeur triste Je suis heureux d'avoir posé ma question à la petite souris.

Tea Malvoisin, l'Âge 10

Je me suis toujours demandé pourquoi la faim existe encore dans le monde. Ça me rend triste de savoir que d'autres enfants n'ont pas de nourriture. Alors, j'ai posé la question à une petite souris que je connais. Elle m'a dit que si chacun partageait ce qu'il possède, plus personne n'aurait faim. La petite souris a rajouté que chacun a quelque chose à donner. Si on n'a pas d'argent on a au moins un sourire à partager. Un sourire ne coûte rien mais il peut réchauffer un coeur triste. Je suis heureux d'avoir posé ma question à la petite souris.

Tea Malvoisin, 10 ans, Ottawa, ON
École Saint-Marie

I've always wondered why teachers don't ride the school bus with kids. Once, my teacher's car blew up. My bus driver said, "Hop on!" My teacher screamed and ran all the way to school! There were ninety-nine kids on the bus. That's too noisy for a teacher! Once, my principal's van hit a tree. My bus driver said "Hop on!" My principal screamed and took a taxi to school! The kids were having a karaoke contest. That's too noisy for a principal! I'd never go on a bus with teachers. They'd just read. That's too quiet for a kid!!

Kate Martin, 8

I've always wondered why teachers don't ride the school bus with kids. Once, my teacher's car blew up. My bus driver said, "Hop on!" My teacher screamed and ran all the way to school! There were ninety-nine kids on the bus. That's too noisy for a teacher! Once, my principal's van hit a tree. My bus driver said "Hop on!" My principal screamed and took a taxi to school! The kids were having a karaoke contest. That's too noisy for a principal! I'd never go on a bus with teachers. They'd just read. That's too quiet for a kid!!

Kate Martin, Age 8, Wroxton, SK
Calder

I've always wondered if I could fly. I would be so proud if that happened. I could then fly anywhere in the world, even fly over the tall buildings and see the oceans and land on the beaches. I could even fly with the birds. I also don't have to take my crowded bus, I could just fly to school. I could also visit all my friends and I could fly really fast, high or low. On Christmas, I could be Santa Claus and secretly deliver gifts, that would be the best Christmas ever. I could then drop candies for the kids.

Vibhor Johnathan Mathur, age 9.

I've always wondered if I could fly. I would be so proud if that happened. I could then fly anywhere in the world, even fly over the tall buildings and see the oceans and land on the beaches. I could even fly with the birds. I also don't have to take my crowded bus. I could just fly to school. I could also visit all my friends and I could fly really fast, high or low. On Christmas, I could be Santa Claus and secretly deliver gifts. That would be the best Christmas ever. I could then drop candies for the kids.

Vibhor Johnathan Mathur, Age 9, Vancouver, BC
U. Hill Elementary

I've always wondered if God made Adam and Eve, who made God. It says in the Bible that God made all living things, but it has never said where God came from, or who made him. He couldn't just appear and start the world, he had to be born or created and if so, who created him?. Then you have to ask yourself, if God created Adam and Eve why didn't he create a wife for himself and they have kids instead of creating Jesus. Then you have to think would everyone in the world be related to each other?

Rachael Mattinson   Age 11

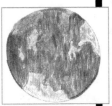

I've always wondered if God made Adam and Eve, who made God. It says in the Bible that God made all living things, but it has never said where God came from, or who made him. He couldn't just appear and start the world. He had to be born or created and if so, who created him? Then you have to ask yourself, if God created Adam and Eve why didn't he created a wife for himself and they have kids instead of creating Jesus. Then you have to think would everyone in the world be related to each other?

Rachael Mattinson, Age 11, Pictou County, NS
Dr. W.A. MacLeod Elementary

I've always wondered what it would be like to be the tall spruce tree outside of my bedroom window. If I was the spruce tree, I would be able to see my school. The only problem would be that I could not walk anywhere. I wouldn't be able to visit any neat places like the Eiffel Tower, the C.N Tower, the Grand Canyon and other inteseting places I can visit in the world. However, I would have lots of birds that live in my long branches to tell me stories about all the beautiful things they get to see.

Brittany McCandless, 12

I've always wondered what it would be like to be the tall spruce tree outside of my bedroom window. If I was the spruce tree I would be able to see my school. The only problem would be that I could not walk anywhere. I wouldn't be able to visit any neat places like the Eiffel Tower, the CN Tower, the Grand Canyon and other interesting places I can visit in the world. However, I would have lots of birds to live on my long branches to tell me stories about all the beautiful things they get to see.

Brittany McCandless, Age 12, St. Thomas, ON
Homedale P.S.

I've always wondered what it would be like to fly. I've seen birds, butterflies, and bugs fly and I've always wanted to be like them. Once I tried to fly like a kite but I was too tall and got stuck in a tree. Then I tried to be a flying crocodile! The way I did that was I took my brother's crocodile Halloween costume and my princess wings. That's how I did that but it just didn't work. Then I figured that I'd better just leave the flying to the things that can fly.

Rebecca Mezzaluna 8

I've always wondered what it would be like to fly. I've seen birds, butterflies, and bugs fly and I've always wanted to be like them. Once I tried to fly like a kite but I was too tall and got stuck in a tree. Then I tried to be a flying crocodile! The way I did that was I took my brother's crocodile Halloween costume and my princess wings. That's how I did that but it just didn't work. Then I figured that I'd better just leave the flying to the things that can fly.

Rebecca Mezzaluna, Age 8, St-Leonard, QC
General Vanier

I've always wonderd why don't people stop to see in this big world what God Created. He created the flowers that are multicolored. He created the white puffy clouds. He created everything even you and me. He painted the trees emerald green. He also made butterflys that have such pretty colors. God also gave us light so we can see. God made day and night. So even if I dont win a prize I just hope Some day Soon people will stop to look at Gods creation and take the time to read about it in his word the Bible.

Rebecca Michl Age 10

I've always wondered why don't people stop to see in this big world that God created. He created the flowers that are multi-coloured. He created the white puffy clouds. He created everything, even you and me. He painted the trees emerald green. He also made butterflies that have such pretty colours. God also gave us light so we can see. God made day and night. So even if I don't win a prize I just hope someday soon people will stop to look at God's creation and take the time to read about it in his word the Bible.

Rebecca Michl, Age 10, Calgary, AB
Home-schooled

I've always wondered why, when you are driving down a road, you see a single shoe lying on the side of a very busy highway. Maybe kids don't like the shoes their parents buy them so they throw them onto the side of the road. Maybe before people get into their car they place their shoes on the rooftop and drive off in a rush forgetting they're there. Maybe they try to air their shoes out by hanging them out the window and accidentally drop them. Whatever the reason, it always amazes me to see shoes littering the roadside.

Eleanor Miller, 11 yrs.

I've always wondered why, when you are driving down a road, you see a single shoe lying on the side of a very busy highway. Maybe kids don't like the shoes their parents buy them so they throw them onto the side of the road. Maybe before people get into their car they place their shoes on the rooftop and drive off in a rush forgetting they're there. Maybe they try to air their shoes out by hanging them out of the window and accidentally drop them. Whatever the reason, it always amazes me to see shoes littering the roadside.

Eleanor Miller, Age 11, North Gower, ON
Turnbull School

I've always wondered how you would feel on a winter day, when the sky is gray, and the day is almost gone. You're outside making a snowman, when a snowflake comes along. It falls down, gently, silently, and almost touches the ground. But it lands on your mitt, and look what you've found. A little, cold, flake, with many different designs, that twirl, and twist in white. The sun is going down, your snowflake begins to melt. You've done all you could to save it. It's beauty lost forever. How many other snowflakes will go unnoticed as they fall silently.

KAILEE MINER

I've always wondered how you would feel on a winter day when they sky is gray, and the day is almost gone. You're outside making a snowman, when a snowflake comes along. It falls down, gently, silently, and almost touches the ground. But it lands on your mitt, and look what you've found. A little cold, flake, with many different designs, that twirl and twist in the white. The sun is going down, your snowflake begins to melt. You've done all you could to save it. Its beauty lost forever. How many other snowflakes will go unnoticed as they fall silently.

Kailee Miner, Age 11, Beaconsfield, QC
Beacon Hill

I've always wondered where the sunset goes after it melts into the sea. Drowning inch by inch, its shaky reflection on the water is replaced by the eerie but magical reflection of the moon. The clouds that were once orange and pink have turned cold grey, as if they were ghosts hovering in the sky. The seagulls that crowded the sky have disappeared and their annoying cries have gone mute. The stars glitter, looking like precious gold. The palm trees sway gently. But the sun will rise again, casting its reflection upon the ripples of the sea.

Sara Mirali, 12

I've always wondered where the sunset goes after it melts into the sea. Drowning inch by inch, its shaky reflection on the water is replaced by the eerie but magical reflection of the moon. The clouds that were once orange and pink have turned cold and grey, as if they were ghosts hovering in the sky. The seagulls that crowded the sky have disappeared and their annoying cries have gone mute. The stars glitter, looking like precious gold. The palm trees sway gently. But the sun will rise again, casting its reflection upon the ripples of the sea.

Sara Mirali, Age 12, Whitby, ON
Sir Samuel Steele P.S.

Je me suis toujours demandé ce que pensent les animaux.
Comme les chiens, si on a un os dans la main, ils pensent
peut-être « Donne-moi l'os s'il-vous-plaît, » ou le cheval
« Enlève-toi de moi. » Si on savait comment les animaux se
sentent, le monde serait meilleur. Peut-être qu'on apprendrait
que les singes n'aiment pas les bananes, que les requins aiment
croquer les roches, on saurait quand un lion a mal aux dents
et quand le chat veut qu'on arrête de le flatter. À cause de ça,
on pourrait être ami avec des animaux féroces.

Philippe Miriello, 10 ans, Montréal, QC
Notre Dame de Fatima

I've always wondered why the monster under my bed only comes out at night. Is it because he does not want anyone to see his ugly face or is he allergic to sunlight? I wouldn't be scared of him anyway, he's just a big, green, purple, slimey guy who likes to scare kids for I don't know why! When you think about it, it's actually kind of silly, I think he is just scared of people noticing him, I mean if I looked like that I would be scared too!

Melanie Mitchell, Age: 11

I've always wondered why the monster under my bed only comes out at night. Is it because he does not want anyone to see his ugly face or is he allergic to sunlight? I wouldn't be scared of him anyway, he's just a big green, purple, slimey guy who likes to scare kids, for I don't know why! When you think about it, it's actually kind of silly, I think he is just scared of people noticing him, I mean if I looked like that I would be scared too!

Melanie Mitchell, Age 11, Ottawa, ON
Sawmill Creek E.S.

I've always wondered what teachers do in the teachers lounge? You never know because of the fact that your not allowed to peek in there at all. If I were to guess what's in there I would say that there's footbaths, hot tubs, doughnuts, video games and all kinds of things like that. Teachers are desperate to get out of class and to get to that humongous party in the teacher's lounge. Maybe even meetings are when teachers sit in big hot tubs with their swimming suits on. I've always wondered this because there was a popcorn smell and it was coming from the teacher's lounge.

Danielle Nahdee, 10

I've always wondered what teachers do in the teacher's lounge? You never know because of the fact you're not allowed to peek in there at all. If I were to guess what's in there I would say that there's footbaths, hot tubs, donuts, video games and all kinds of things like that. Teachers are desperate to get out of class and get to that humungus party in the teacher's lounge. Maybe even meetings are when teachers sit in big hot tubs with their swimming suits on. I've wondered this because there was a popcorn smell coming from the teachers' lounge.

Danielle Nahdee, Age 10, Sarnia, ON
Queen Elizabeth II

I've always wondered if the guy made out of sugar would survive. The guy made out of sugar went for a walk in the rainforest every day. It rained there almost every day there. one day he took a walk in the rainforest and he melted. Now he was eighty seven centimetres tall. The next day he went again and he didn't melt, he grew. He was a thousand centimetres tall. He never had a walk in The rainforest again. He is going to have walks in the desert. He will hopefully not melt.

Emma Neale age 9

I've always wondered if the guy made out of sugar would survive.
The guy made out of sugar went for a walk in the rainforest every
day. It rained almost every day there. One day he took a walk in
the rainforest and he melted. Now he was eighty seven centimetres
tall. The next day he went again and he didn't melt. He grew.
He was a thousand centimetres tall. He never had a walk in
the rainforest again. He is going to have walks in the desert.
He will hopefully not melt.

Emma Neale, Age 9, Beaconsfield, QC
Windermere Elementary

I've always wondered, can teddy bears talk? Do stuffed animals, dolls, action figures, and puppets really talk? Do they have a watch doll or something to tell if a human is coming or waking up? Do they play games like Trouble, Twister, Tag, Golf, Volleyball, Soccer, and Hide-And-Go-Seek? I wonder if they bake cookies, cakes, pies, and muffins? Iv always wondered, do teddy bears talk?

Jamie Newel 10

I've always wondered, can teddy bears talk? Do stuffed animals, dolls, action figures, and puppets really talk? Do they have a watch doll or something to tell if a human is coming or waking up? Do they play games like trouble, twister, tag, golf, volleyball, soccer and hide-and-go-seek? I wonder if they bake cookies, cakes, and pies and muffins? I've always wondered, do teddy bears talk?

Jamie Newel, Age 10, Surrey, BC
Crescent Park Elementary

I've always wondered what your pets do when you're away. I think the dogs go out and play poker, the cats, they go to the spa, hamsters go to the gym. Guinea pigs go to all you can eat buffets, bunnies play bingo. Horses are in apple bobbing contests and sheep go to old folks' homes to knit. Goats go to the boxing arena and fight, cows have tea parties and pigs have pancake breakfast all day. Fish go and visit their mermaid friends and they all return home before their owners. That's what I've always wondered.

Alex Odribege, Age 9, Richmond, BC
Manoah Steves Elementry

I've always wondered what it would be like if we were all the same. If we all had the same name, same hair and same colour skin, the same interests and pasttimes oh what trouble we'd be in! We wouldn't know who was who, if the person in the mirror was me or you! We'd do the same things day in and day out. If we had a world like this I'd want to shout! So it's good to be different in our own special way, learning, laughing, and seizing the day!

Paige O'Neill   age 11

I've always wondered what it would be like if we were all the same. If we all had the same name, same hair and same colour skin, the same interests and past-times oh what trouble we'd be in! We wouldn't know who was who, if the person in the mirror was me or you! We'd do the same things day in and day out. If we had a world like this I'd want to shout! So it's good to be different in our own special way, learning, laughing, and seizing the day!

Paige O'Neill, Age 11, Annan, ON
Notre Dame Catholic School

I've always wondered how trees are alive but they never move. I think it started that millions of years ago trees would walk around, talk with their friends, play games and even drink. But how come they don't move now? Well that's because one day they got so tired, they just wanted to sleep, so they planted themselves to sleep. Sometimes at night when everything is quiet you could still them snore. I still think that one of these days the trees are going to wake up and laugh and play like they used to. The End!

Jaclyn Onofre, Age 10, Laval, QC
John F. Kennedy School

I've always wondered what would life be like without colour? I think the world would be much duller. Although racism would not exist, Multiculturalism would be missed. Rainbows and flowers, and green grass too, would no longer have such beautiful hues. Nothing would be unique or catch your eye, not even the bright sun or the blue sky. Kids would no longer smile at the zoo, no tiger stripes or the colour of a cockatoo. Clothing would be ever so plain, fashion would no longer remain. So the next time you look outside appreciate the colours and have some pride.

Rebeka O'Regan age 8

I've always wondered what would life be like without colour? I think the world would be much duller. Although racism would not exist, multiculturalism would be missed. Rainbows and flowers and green grass too, would no longer have such beautiful hues. Nothing would be unique or catch your eye, not even the bright sun or the blue sky. Kids would no longer smile at the zoo, no tiger stripes or the colour of a cockatoo. Clothing would be ever so plain, fashion would no longer remain. So the next time you look outside, appreciate our colours and have some pride.

Rebeka O'Regan, Age 8, Guelph, ON
Sir Isaac Brock P.S.

"I've always wondered what it's like above the sea," said the black minnow. He was in school. "Very good!" said his teacher. "Your homework is to answer your question," she said to the school. So the black minnow started swimming to the top of the sea. At the same time, a fisherman was putting out his net in the middle of the sea. The black minnow swam into the net and was caught! The fisherman gave the black minnow to his daughter for a pet. He got a nice big aquarium. He found out what its like above the sea!

Claire Pageau, Age 11

"I've always wondered what it's like above the sea," said the black minnow. He was in school. "Very good!" said his teacher. "Your homework is to answer your question," she said to the school. So the black minnow started swimming to the top of the sea. At the same time, a fisherman was putting out his net in the middle of the sea. The black minnow swam into the net and was caug ht! The fisherman gave the black minnow to his daughter as a pet. He got a nice big aquarium. He found out what it's like above the sea!

Claire Pageau, Age 11, Stittsville, ON
Ottawa Waldorf School

I've Always wondered....

What life would be like if everything
was backwards. What if parents did
our chores and went to school while
kids watched t.v.? What if fruit
and vegies were bad for you and
candy was very healthy. What if
junk food at every meal was
good? What if more t.v. made
you smarter and homework made
you dumb? What if not bathing
made you smell good? or not
cleaning your room was a good
thing? If kids were in charge,
life would be so simple! this is
getting scary! so i think i will stop.
Maybe....

Christy Papadopoulos 12yrs Age!

I've always wondered what life would be like if everything was
backwards. What if parents did our chores and went to school
while kids watched TV? What if fruit and veggies were bad for
you and candy was very healthy? What if junk food at every
meal was good? What is more TV made you smarter and
homework made you dumb? What if not bathing made you
smell good? Or not cleaning your room was a good thing?
If kids were in charge life would be so simple! This is getting
scary! So I think I will stop. Maybe…

Christy Papadopoulos, Age 12, Edmonton, AB
Killarney School

Je me suis toujours demandé ce que serait le monde sans humain. Est-ce qu'il y aurait des animaux ? Si oui, que feraient-ils? Est-ce qu'ils mangeraient et boiraient du thé à la table ? Cela serait drôlement bizarre ! Ils pourraient aller  magasiner comme nous… Ils auraient des emplois. Les boeufs seraient menuisiers, les cygnes seraient vendeurs et les chats artistes ! Des animaux feraient la cuisine et le ménage. Pendant que d'autres animaux répareraient la maison et ramasseraient l'argent. Dommage que cela ne soit qu'un rêve. À bien y penser peut-être sur une autre planète.

Alexandra Paradis, 11 ans, St-Jean-sur-Richelieu, QC
École Notre-Dame-du-Sacré-Coeur

I've always wondered what it would be like as a horse. Running through the woods and meadows, feeling the wind blow through my mane, and feeling the sand on my hooves. Playing all day with my friends, watching over my peers in case of danger, and making sure we are still together when we change places. Life would be different, but almost the same, as humans. I am born as a colt, who grows up to be a beautiful stallion. Fortunately, my love and passion for these beautiful creatures will never change, even though I can't change WHO I AM.

Krysta Phillips   11 years old

I've always wondered what it would be like as a horse. Running through the woods and the meadows, feeling the wind blow through my mane and feeling the sand on my hooves. Playing all day with my friends, watching over my peers in case of danger, and making sure we are still together when we change places. Life would be different but almost the same, as humans. I am born as a colt, who grows up to be a beautiful stallion. Fortunately, my love and passion for these beautiful creatures will never change, even though I can't change who I am.

Krysta Phillips, Age 11, Chelmsford, ON
École Publique Pavillon de l'Avenir

I've always wondered...
   When I go to sleep at the end
of a busy day, why my body needs
rest. When bedtime comes, my mind
works differently. Behind my closed
eyes a new world appears.
   Dreams give me feelings of
happiness, anger, fear and sadness.
They can be colourful, wonderful,
and magical. I once dreamt of
being a royal princess. I lived in
a castle made of glitter. It
was one hundred feet high and
sparkled beautifully. I had
everything I ever wanted.
This dream made me very
happy. I guess that's why I
need rest at night. Sweet Dreams.
                   Sara Piccott, Age 12

I've always wondered when I go to sleep at the end of a busy day, why my body needs rest. When bedtime comes, my mind works differently. Behind my closed eyes a new world appears. Dreams give me feelings of happiness, anger, fear and sadness. They can be colourful, wonderful, and magical. I once dreamt of being a royal princess. I lived in a castle made of glitter. It was one hundred feet high and sparkled beautifully. I had everything I ever wanted. This dream made me very happy. I guess that's why I need rest at night. Sweet dreams.

Sara Piccott, Age 12, Syndney, NS
Thompson Jr. High School

I've always wondered how it would be like to fly. I could follow birds and fly close to airplanes. Up high, I could see my house. It would be smaller than a mouse! Maybe I could fly into space. Actually, I am almost there. Wow! There are so many stars! The moon is so big and bright. Also, if I could fly I would be able to see all the countries, oceans and lakes all over the world. What a beautiful sight, I'm sure! So I will always wonder how it would be like to fly.

Nicole-Anne Pilon, Age 10, Mississauga, ON
René-Lamoureux

Je me suis toujours demandé pourquoi les grenouilles ont une grosse boule au bout de leurs doigts, jusqu'à ce que je découvre une histoire et je tiens à vous la raconter. C'est l'histoire d'une jeune grenouille qui voulait devenir plus jolie. Elle était très pauvre. Elle vivait dans un sac qu'une jeune fille avait laissé tomber. Un jour, la petite grenouille qui se nommait Baltivia, décida d'aller voir le magicien, Monsieur Capoudalbou. Il accepta de la rendre jolie. Malheureusement, il manqua son coup et mit une boule au bout des doigts de chaque grenouille.

Emilie Pimparé, 10 ans, Repentigny, QC
École Louis-Fréchette

I've always wondered where the tooth fairy lives maybe she lives somewhere in the bushes and stuff her house might be made of teeth or maybe she keeps the teeth so she can put them in babies mouths. The tooth fairy is a very nice fairy and is always happy she likes to sleep during the day and goes around ~~at money~~ to houses at night to get teeth and give money to children. After she is all done getting the teeth she goes and visits the other faries and they play and talk until she has to go to bed.

Ashley Poirier. 7

I've always wondered where the tooth fairy lives. Maybe she lives somewhere in the bushes and stuff. Her house might be made of teeth or maybe she keeps the teeth so she can put them in babies' mouths. The tooth fairy is a very nice fairy and is always happy. She likes to sleep during the day and goes around to houses at night to get teeth and give money to children. After she is all done getting the teeth she goes and visits the other fairies and they play and talk until she has to go to bed.

Ashley Poirier, Age 7, Sudbury, ON
Circle of Friends

I've always wondered how Turtle got his shell. Dad says there was once a small, kind turtle named Hishala who had only soft body parts. When predators came, Hishala had to run to his special hiding place and the other animals would always laugh at him. His fastest enemy was Cheetah. One day when Cheetah came, Hishala's hiding place was being built over! Then suddenly, a splotch of cement fell on his back. So he decided to go back home. On the way home some leaves fell on his back, forming a shell that all of his children would have.

By: Ethan Poirier, age 9

I've always wondered how Turtle got his shell. Dad says there was once a small, kind turtle name Hishala who had only soft body parts. When predators came, Hishala had to run to a special hiding place and the other animals would always laugh at him. His fastest enemy was Cheetah. One day when Cheetah came, Hishala's hiding place was being built over! Then suddenly, a splotch of cement fell on his back. So he decided to go back home. On the way home some leaves fell on his back, forming a shell that all of his children would have.

Ethan Poirier, Age 9, Camrose, AB
St. Patrick's School

I've always wondered what my cat would say
if she could speak?
Would she be bold
or maybe meek?
Would she be a genius
and cure a disease or two?
Or would she be really snotty and say,
"Girl, that outfit does NOT suit you!"
Would she help me sort out my life?
Or maybe end world strife?
But the most likely thing she would say,
is what she is saying today!
Though all we hear are meows,
when she sits by her food bowl and howls.
If she could speak,
She would not lead me.
She would say,
"Feed me!"
Jamie Ponomar, age 12

I've always wondered what my cat would say if she could speak.
Would she be bold, or maybe meek? Would she be a genius,
and cure a disease or two? Or would she be really snotty, and
say "Girl, that outfit does NOT suit you!" Would she help me
sort out my life? Or maybe end world strife? But the most likely
thing she would say is what she is saying today! Though all we
hear are meows, when she sits by her food bowl and howls.
If she could speak she would not lead me, she would say,
"Feed me!"

Jamie Ponomar, Age 12, Lethbridge, AB
G.S. Lakie Middle School

I've always wondered what it would be like to be a cat. To be able to go to sleep anytime, or to be able to go out as far as I wanted. Cats are fun and soft and sometimes funny. If I were a cat I'd catch flies and chase mice. I would jump at grasshoppers and find other cats to play with. The most favourite thing I'd do if I were a cat I would find a sunny spot, stretch out, put my paws over my head and sleep for hour after hour after hour after hour after hour.

Janessa Pudwell 8

I've always wondered what it would be like to be a cat. To be able to go to sleep anytime, or to be able to go out as far as I wanted. Cats are fun and soft and sometimes funny. If I were a cat I'd catch flies and chase mice. I would jump at grasshoppers and find other cats to play with. The most favourite thing I'd do if I were a cat I would find a sunny spot, stretch out, put my paws over my head and sleep for hour after hour after hour after hour after hour.

Janessa Pudwell, Age 8, Medicine Hat, AB
Crestwood School

I've always wondered why I was kidnapped. I was eating tuna sandwiches peacefully on the beach when a slimy tentacle grabbed my wrist. "Hey!" I gurgled while being dragged into the water deeper and deeper. Finally we stopped at a cavern. Four octopuses waited. I closed my eyes, ready to die. The boss octopus bubbled sternly, "Calm down Land Creature, we're not going to eat you, just prosecute you for eating tuna. That's a serious offence however; we're going straight to the death penalty!" Suddenly a colossal tidal wave crashed, hurling me back to shore. I calmly finished my sandwiches.

McKenzie Rainey, Age 11

I've always wondered why I was kidnapped. I was eating tuna sandwiches peacefully on the beach when a slimy tentacle grabbed my wrist. "Hey!" I gurgled while being dragged into the water deeper and deeper. Finally we stopped at a cavern. Four octopuses waited. I closed my eyes, ready to die. The boss octopus bubbled sternly, "Calm down Land Creature, we're not going to eat you, just prosecute you for eating tuna. That's a serious offence however; we're going straight to the death penalty!" Suddenly a colossal tidal wave crashed, hurling me back to shore. I calmly finished my sandwiches.

McKenzie Rainey, Age 11, Vancouver, BC
Upper Lynn Elementary

I've always wondered how parrots got their colours. I came up with an explanation. Back when parrots were black, and rainbows were made by hand, there lived a clumsy parrot. One day after a hard rain, this parrot went flying. The animals that made the rainbows were busy painting the sky. The parrot was flying in circles and loops, left and right. When he straightened out he didn't see the wet rainbow ahead. He flew right into it! He was covered in paint of all colours. From then on all the parrots that were born were born in bright colour.

Tess Raithby   age: 12

I've always wondered how parrots got their colours. I came up with an explanation. Back when parrots were black, and rainbows were made by hand, there lived a clumsy parrot. One day after a hard rain, this parrot went flying. The animals that made the rainbows were busy painting the sky. The parrot was flying in circles and loops, left and right. When he straightened out he didn't see the wet rainbow ahead. He flew right into it! He was covered in paint of all colours. From then on all the parrots that were born were born in bright colour.

Tess Raithby, Age 12, Nanaimo, BC
Rutherford School

I've always wondered what life would be like if we only had one season which was winter. We would all have to survive the cold all life long. Children would catch colds which they gave to other children, and the stores won't sell popsicles or icecream. Imagine if it snowed every single day making the temperature drop to about minus twenty five. Some teachers even probably won't let us go outside because of the extreme cold. Just thinking of winter gives me goosebumps, thinking of the chilly weather. Would you like a cold, chilly, miserable everlasting season such as winter?

Shivsha Rajkumar, Age 11

I've always wondered what life would be like if we only had one season which was winter. We would all have to survive the cold all life long. Children would catch colds which they gave to other children. And the stores won't sell popsicles or ice cream. Imagine if it snowed every single day making the temperature drop to about minus twenty-five. Some teachers even probably won't let us go outside because of the extreme cold. Just thinking of winter gives me goosebumps, thinking of the chilly weather. Would you like a cold, chilly, miserable, everlasting season such as winter?

Shivsha Rajkumar, Age 11, Ottawa, ON
Carleton Heights P.S.

I've always wondered if a family or a person coming to Canada, from another country, will they try something new or learn new things? I think the family or person will feel lonely because they might not have any family members in Canada, but they do in their country. They maybe don't know how to speak English well, so they might have a hard time speaking English. When years are passing by, they have learned English and new things. Well now they have learned English and new things about Canada they would have no promables by then.

Medea Rasheed, 11 years

I've always wondered if a family or a person coming to Canada, from another country, will they try something new or learn new things? I think the family or person will feel lonely because they might not have any family members in Canada, but they do in their country. They maybe don't know how to speak English well, so they might have a hard time speaking English. When years are passing by, they have learned English and new things. Well now they have learned English and new thing about Canada they would have no problems by then.

Medea Rasheed, Age 11, Waterloo, ON
Cedarbrae School

I've always wondered how the stars got in the sky. One day in a small village there was a man named Septora. He looked at the sky and thought it was too plain. All there was was the moon. The other villagers agreed and they were all thinking of how they could make the night sky better. That night Septora saw alot of fireflies flying around. He had an idea. So he got a few jars with lids and caught the fireflies. Then he stood on his house and let them go in the sky.
He called them stars!

Tiffani Richards-Hughes   10 yrs. old

I've always wondered how the stars got in the sky. One day in a small village there was a man named Septora. He looked at the sky, and thought it was too plain. All there was was the moon. The other villagers agreed and they were all thinking of how they could make the night sky better. That night Septora saw a lot of fireflies flying around. He had an idea. So he got a few jars with lids and caught the fireflies. Then he stood on his house and let them go in the sky. He called them stars!

Tiffani Richards-Hughes, Age 10, Sudbury, ON
Adamsdale P.S.

I've always wondered what love was truly about. I don't quite know yet, but I do know that love can change as fast as the autumn breeze. That love is like a rose, beautiful, yet if not properly taken care of, will wither away. Some say there is no need for such a thing. How very wrong they are. Without it, the world would be lost. I believe it is a powerful gift that will never die and I hope it will bring you happiness.

Chelsi Robichaud, Age 11

I've always wondered what love was truly about. I don't quite know yet, but I do know that love can change directions as fast as the autumn breeze. That love is like a rose, beautiful, yet if not properly taken care of, will wither away. Some say there is no need for such a thing. How very wrong they are. Without it, the world would be lost. I believe it is a powerful gift that will never die and I hope it will bring you happiness.

Chelsi Robichaud, Age 11, Dartmouth, NS
École Bois-Joli

I've always wondered why the leaves change colours. I think because angels from above came and sprinkle paint on them in the fall. The leaves are: red, orange, yellow, green and brown. The angles have so much fun and make the leaves so colourful. The leaves are so beautiful in the sunshine that they sparkle. When the angles cry up in Heaven it makes wind and rain. The leaves fall to the ground, the angles cry because winter is coming and there isn't very much sunshine. Angles don't like the cold, snow and strong winds. The angles pray for Spring. The End

Nicole Rock 7 years old

I've always wondered why the leaves change colours. I think because angels from above came and sprinkled paint on them in the fall. The leaves are: red, orange, yellow, green and brown. The angels have so much fun and make the leaves so colourful. The leaves are so beautiful in the sunshine that they sparkle. When the angels cry up in Heaven it makes wind and rain. The leaves fall to the ground, the angels cry because winter is coming and there isn't very much sunshine. Angels don't like the cold, snow and strong winds. The angels pray for spring.

Nicole Rock, Age 7, Orangeville, ON
St. Peter's

I've always wondered about a dream I had one day on a dock.
My dream was that I was on a beach on a glorious day. Suddenly,
a sea monster rose from the shallows. I froze. It lowered its head
to eat me, but it didn't, surprisingly. Instead it told me of gliding
through the deep waters, snapping at pickerel, his favourite food.
His name was Fred and he led a happy life. I became his friend
and rode him around the lake. Then I woke up and guess what?
I found a piece of seaweed in my ear.

Nathan Ruston, Age 10, Comox, BC
Brooklyn Elementary School

I've always wondered how the sun was formed. I like to think that a long time ago, before the earth was created, the sun was a tiny star. I imagine that the star grew and grew and grew until it was bigger than the other stars. Then I think God gave the star powers so it could shine down on the earth and give people light and warmth and beauty. When all of this happened it must have been a lovely sight! I love to watch the sunset at my cottage and I wonder about this every time I do!

Lauren Rzepecki, age 9

I've always wondered how the sun was formed. I like to think that a long time ago, before the earth was created, the sun was a tiny star. I imagine that the star grew and grew and grew until it was bigger than the other stars. Then I think God gave the star powers so it could shine down the earth and give people light and warmth and beauty. When all of this happened it must have been a lovely sight! I love to watch the sunset at my cottage and I wonder about this every time I do!

Lauren Rzepecki, Age 9, Oakville, ON
St. Marguerite d'Youville

I've always wondered what it feels like to be a fish. It must be fascinating breathing underwater. Swimming might feel like soaring through the air and waving your arms like the wings of a bird. Having gills would feel kind of odd almost like breathing through your cheeks. What spooks me out is that one eye turn right and the other will turn left. Yikes! I wonder if fish have friends or families? We hear about school of fish but do they really go to school like me? Do you think they have swimming contests instead of writing contests?

Isra Sabunju, Age 9, Ottawa, ON
Elemdale Public School

I've always wondered if I could fly.
I'd fly through the air and reach the sky.
I can imagine myself spreading wings,
and amazingly doing many other things.
I'd fly through the air at the latest hour,
and underneath me would stand the CN Tower.
I'd see the views as I fly in the air,
while the wind would blow through my hair.
This imaginary flying experience makes me feel
tall, because being in the sky makes
everyone on land look small. Soon I notice
my imagination has carried me away, and
now I'm back to life as it is today.

Erum Saleem Age: 12

I've always wondered if I could fly. I'd fly through the air and reach the sky. I can imagine myself spreading wings, and amazingly doing many other things. I'd fly through the air at the latest hour, and underneath me would stand the CN Tower. I'd see the views as I fly in the air, while the wind would blow through my hair. This imaginary flying experience makes me feel tall, because being in the sky makes everyone on land look small. Soon I notice my imagination has carried me away, and now I'm back to life as it is today.

Erum Saleem, Age 12, Kingston, ON
Calvin Park

I've always wondered what it would be like to be a mermaid. I wonder what they look like, where they live and what they eat. If I were a mermaid I would want blond hair and a purple fish tail. I would want to live in a colourful coral reef. I would swim around looking for tropical fish and beautiful shells along the ocean floor. I would go in all the sunken ships and try on all the jewellery in the treasure chests. Then I would go to a quiet place and dream about being a little girl.

Marina Santarossa, Age 9, Windsor, ON
Southwood School

I've always wondered, where does the white go when the snow melts? I mean, most people know that snow vaporizes and becomes rain, but where does the white go? Does it go with the snow and become fluffy white clouds or stay on the earth and become as green as grass? Snow might run into a river and into the sea, but where does the white go? Is it harvested to make paper or shot into space to make twinkling stars? Well, that is what I've always wondered!

Kyle Scholl, age 11

I've always wondered where does the white go when the snow melts? I mean, most people know that the snow vaporizes and becomes rain, but where does the white go? Does it go with the snow and become fluffy white clouds or stay on the earth and become as green as grass? Snow might run into a river and into the sea, but were does the white go? Is it harvested to make paper or shot into space to make twinkling stars? Well, that is what I've always wondered!

Kyle Schole, Age 11, Pickardville, AB
Busby Elementary

175

I've always wondered what would happen if there was no sun or moon. It would be dark all the time. It would always be night. One day a witch came by and took away the sun and moon. The people were so mad. But they loved sleeping. But still they were going to get the witch back. So they blasted into outer space and found the sun and moon. The people pushed and pushed until the sun and moon were back in their spots. The sun and moon will never leave us again. The End.

Emily Schuldis, Age 8, Bowmanville, ON
Knox Christian

I've always wondered why Michigan is shaped like a mitten and Italy like a boot. Maybe when God made land he baked it as a cookie. After God used cookie stencils to divide the countries. First God used a mitten and a boot. Unfortunately the calligrapher was hard of hearing. For "mitten" he wrote "Michigan." Next God said "That boot will fit Aly my daughter." The deaf calligrapher only heart "It Aly" so he wrote "Italy." In a fit of frustration God nibbled the leftover crumbs, and left the world to the inhabitants to divide and name as they wished.

Ezra Schwartz, Age 11, Westmount, QC
St-George's School of Montreal

I've always wondered what it would be like to fly like a bird. I would love to feel the fresh clean air under my wings. What a gift it would be to dance in the fluffy clouds without any cares. I would soar over glistening oceans, tall snowcapped mountains, and golden prairies. The wind would be music to my ears. It would take me to great heights and bring me down to gentle green grass. I would drift for hours on a warm jet stream just to see where it takes me. I can only imagine the complete freedom.

Tayler Sharp age 10

I've always wondered what if would be like to fly like a bird. I would love to feel the fresh clean air under my wings. What a gift it would be to dance in the fluffy clouds without any cares. I would soar over glistening oceans, tall snow-capped mountains and golden prairies. The wind would be music to my ears. It would take me to great heights and bring me down to gentle green grass. I would drift for hours on a warm jet stream just to see where it takes me. I can only imagine the complete freedom.

Tayler Sharp, Age 10, Maple Ridge, BC
Yennadon Elementary

I've always wondered why the clouds were so white! They must be so comfortably softer than any pillow you can ever imagine! Clouds may be different colours each day! White, red, yellow, pink every day many colours start to appear. They are so cool in every way! Just think what you can do. I would use it for a new bed, pillows too! I would be so well rested for the rest of my days. I've always wanted to go, live in the cloud world. I will only dream of it every day of my wonderful life! I only dream!

Cheyenne Simon, Age 12

I've always wondered why the clouds were so white! They must be so comfortably softer than any pillow you can ever imagine! Clouds may be different colours each day! White, red, yellow, pink every day many colours start to appear. They are so cool in every way! Just think what you can do. I would use it for a new bed, pillows too! I would be so well rested for the rest of my days. I've always wanted to go live in the cloud world. I will only dream of it every day of my wonderful life! I only dream!

Cheyenne Simon, Age 12, Kanehsatake, QC
Ratihente High School

I've always wondered what would happen if a martian told me to vacuum Pluto. I would say sure! Then I would race into my spaceship and zoom off to Pluto. On the way I ran out of gas and then I went to Mars and got some more fuel. I finally got to Pluto. My vacuum is big and tall. The colors of it are black and red. I am going to vacuum on Pluto. I am very scared because no one has ever been to Pluto before. Vacuuming is so much fun. I am going to stay here on Pluto forever.

Kurtis Simpson – 10 years

I've always wondered what would happen if a martian told me to vacuum Pluto. I would say sure! Then I would race into my spaceship and zoom off to Pluto. On the way I ran out of gas and then I went to Mars and got some more fuel. I finally got to Pluto. My vacuum is big and tall. The colours of it are black and red. I am going to vacuum on Pluto. I am very scared because no one has ever been to Pluto before. Vacuuming is so much fun. I am going to stay here on Pluto forever.

Kurtis Simpson, Age 10, Regina, SK
Stewart Nicks School

I've always wondered where the Tooth Fairy puts all the teeth she collects and where does she get all that money? Maybe she is building a tooth castle and charges for tours to learn how to brush and floss properly. Does she have co-workers, are they all girls and what do they look like? Maybe the tooth fairy sells the teeth to the Dentist so he can make teeth for people who need them. Whatever the Tooth Fairy does, I am sure she must have help because my teeth are always falling out.

Keaton Somers 10

I've always wondered where the Tooth Fairy puts the teeth she collects and where does she get all that money? Maybe she is building a tooth castle and charges for tours to learn how to brush and floss properly. Does she have co-workers, are they all girls and what do they look like? Maybe the Tooth Fairy sells the teeth to the Dentist so he can make teeth for people who need them. Whatever the Tooth Fairy does, I am sure she must have help because my teeth are always falling out.

Keaton Somers, Age 10, Sillikers, NB
North and South Esk Elementary

I've always wondered what it would be like if there were no wars in the world. What would the government do with all the money? Would they give it to the poor living on the streets? What would the army do with all the guns and tanks? Would they just destroy them because no one needed them anymore? Would the army put all the tanks and guns on display all over the world in museums? I think the world would be a happier place without wars. Peace would make the world a better place to live.

Kevin A. Stadnyk age 9

I've always wondered what it would be like if there were no wars in the world. What would the government do with all the money? Would they give it to the poor living on the streets? What would the army do with all the guns and tanks? Would they just destroy them because no one needed them anymore? Would the army put all the tanks and guns on display all over the world in museums? I think the world would be a happier place without wars. Peace would make the world a better place to live.

Kevin A. Stadnyk, Age 9, Sackville, NS
Sackville Heights Elementary

I've always wondered what it would be like to be a bird. Swooping down, sailing over houses. It must be very cozy in that warm nest. I would get to learn the birdy language! I would fly so high up, up. I would fly high over all the people, the hills and all the houses. The treetops will look like flower petals. White fluffy clouds will look like cotton candy. At night the stars will look like big balls of fire! It must be really neat to be a bird.

Adria Standeven 8

I've always wondered what it would be like to be a bird. Swooping down, sailing over houses. It must be very cozy in that warm nest. I would get to learn the birdy language! I would fly so high up, up. I would fly high over all the people, the hills and all the houses. The treetops will look like flower petals. White fluffy clouds will look like cotton candy. At night the stars will look like big balls of fire! It must be really neat to be a bird.

Adria Standeven, Age 8, Tecumseh, ON
A.V. Graham Public School

I've always wondered what it would be like to have a dragon. If it were real I would buy a special egg and hatch a blue Dragon. She could go outside in the daytime and stay under the porch when I go to school and sleep at night in bed with me. When she grew to be a year old I'd start riding her. She could fly me around and take me anywhere I wanted to go. She could make a fire and roast my marshmallows at camp. She would be magical and could turn the bad things into good.

Kaitlyn Staveley   8 age

I've always wondered what it would be like to
have a dragon. If it were real I would buy a
special egg and hatch a blue dragon. She could
go outside in the daytime and stay under the
porch when I go to school and sleep at night in

bed with me. When she grew to be a year old I'd start riding her.
She could fly me around and take me anywhere I wanted to go.
She could make a fire and roast my marshmallows at camp.
She would be magical and could turn the bad things into good.

Kaitlyn Staveley, Age 8, Saint Anicet, QC
Huntingdon Academy

184

I've always wondered when I'm watching TV, what the people on TV are doing at the same time I'm watching the screen. Whether it's a live game hockey or soccer, or a regular program played repeatedly. I wonder whether they are watching TV like me, or sweating in front of a crowd, scoring a goal, taking a hit, reading a book, or surfing the internet. How do they feel? Tired or comfy, exhilerated or exasperated? Gee, there's a lot of things they could be doing, while I'm here, in front of my TV.

Brendan Steele, 12

I've always wondered when I'm watching TV what the people on TV are doing at the same time I'm watching the screen. Whether it's a live game hockey or soccer or a regular program played repeatedly. I wonder whether they are watching TV like me, or sweating in front of a crowd, scoring a goal or taking a hit, reading a book or surfing the internet. How do they feel? Tired or comfy, exhilarated or exasperated? Gee, there's a lot of things they could be doing while I'm here, in front of my TV.

Brendan Steele, Age 12, Vancouver, BC
Braemar Elementary

I've always wondered what it
would be like to be a teddy bear.
Who gives me love,
Who gives me care.
If I were a teddy I would be
cozy and warm.
I would keep them safe through a
frightening storm.
They would tell me secrets I
couldn't tell.
Even the ones I want to scream
and yell.
We could have tea parties everyday,
sing songs and go outside and play.
But at the end of the day we don't
sit and cry because a friendship
like this one could never die.

Eryn Stewart age 12

I've always wondered what it would be like to be a teddy bear.
Who gives me love, who gives me care. If I were a teddy I would
be cozy and warm. I would keep them safe through a frightening
storm. They could tell me secrets I couldn't tell. Even the ones I
want to scream and yell. We could have tea parties every day, sing
songs and go outside and play. But at the end of the day we don't
sit and cry because a friendship like this one could never die.

Eryn Stewart, Age 12, Hamilton, ON
Sacred Heart School

I've always wondered Why friends are important in the World. Without friends life wouldn't be as fun. It's not as fun playing alone. Friends are important in your life because you get to go over to their house. You also get to have sleepovers with them. Birthday parties are full of my friends. At recess you can play on the playground with your friends. Friends are important because you get to talk to them everyday. Without friends you would be bored. I like to talk to my friends about school and other things. You can tell your friends secrets.

Kelsey Stover   8

I've always wondered why friends are important in the world. Without friends life wouldn't be as fun. It's not as fun playing alone. Friends are important in your life because you get to go over to their house. You also get to have sleepovers with them. Birthday parties are full of my friends. At recess you can play on the playground with your friends. Friends are important because you get to talk to them every day. Without friends you would be bored. I like to talk to my friends about school and other things. You can tell your friends secrets.

Kelsey Stover, Age 8, Bowmanville, ON
Ontario St. P.S.

Je me suis toujours demandé si on peut vivre sous l'eau?
Peut-être que si nous passions beaucoup de temps dans l'eau,
on aurait des branchies qui nous pousseraient derrière les oreilles.
On mangerait des poissons et des algues. On pourrait aussi
s'amuser à faire éclater des bulles d'air et à faire peur aux
hippocampes. Il y aurait un dauphin par famille qui nous
permettrait de voyager. Les baleines seraient des transports
en commun. Les poissons clowns organiseraient des cirques.
Les requins seraient les polices. Je crois que la vie pourrait
être agréable sous l'eau.

Isabelle St-Pierre, 11 ans, Ste-Hénédine, QC
École La Découverte

I've always wondered how leaves change and fall to the ground. I know that leaves are green in spring and summer but why do leaves change colour in fall. I like leaves when they are green or red. I think the leaves change colour because they get too old to stay up in a tree. Now I want to know how leaves fall to the ground. I know that leaves stay on the branches of trees in spring and summer but how do leaves fall to the ground? I think that I'am going to learn about leaves soon. I like leaves!

Sumaiya Syed 9 yrs

I've always wondered how leaves change and fall to the ground. I know that leaves are green in spring and summer but why do leaves change colour in fall. I like leaves when they are green or red. I think the leaves change colour because they get too old to stay up in a tree. Now I want to know how leaves fall to the ground. I know that leaves stay on the branches of trees in spring and summer but how do leaves fall to the ground? I think that I am going to learn about leaves soon. I like leaves!

Sumaiya Syed, Age 9, Surrey, BC
Dr. F.D. Sinclair

I've always wondered... Hi. My Name is Miranda and I've always wondered does the fridge light always goes off after shutting the door? Here I am, Miranda Diago, to prove what happens after you get your little midnight snack. This is what I did: I put this little camera in the refrigerator. You wouldn't believe what I saw the next day! I saw the carrots doing the limbo with the potatoes and the ketchup and mustard playingpin the tail on relish! I showed my parents this tape and they said "We better have a barbeque tonight," so we did.

Jessica Talbot, Age 11, Shilo, MB
École Brandon

I've always wondered why grass always stands up. There must be some grass emotions... Some kids were playing ball in a schoolyard. They had really heavy footsteps that flattened all the surrounding grass. The football they were using often fell to the ground. Poor grass, it had been squished and stormed upon by then! Determinedly, the grass decided to stand up for itself. It slowly tilted itself up, and finally stood proudly, having resumed its original stance. The news spread worldwide about the courageous grass, and the moral behind the grass' courage is something that amazes me.

Laurel Tam   – 10

I've always wondered why grass always stands up. There must be some grass emotions… Some kids were playing ball in a schoolyard. They had really heavy footsteps that flattened all the surrounding grass. The football they were using often fell to the ground. Poor grass, it had been squished and stormed upon by then! Determinedly, the grass decided to stand up for itself. It slowly tilted itself up, and finally stood proudly, having resumed its original stance. The news spread worldwide about the courageous grass, and the moral behind the grass' courage is something that amazes me.

Laurel Tam, Age 10, Scarborough, ON
Wesley Christian Academy

I've always wondered what it would be like to be sand on a beach. Being scattered all over, in people's shoes and in the enormous ocean. People coming to visit me every day in the summer. Little kids making sand castles with me. Dogs digging holes in me, burying something, and only I know what it is. On special occasions, I'd watch the bright and colourful fireworks show. But I'll be so lonely in the winter, and in the summer I'd get trampled on by everyone. I guess I'll just stick to being myself... for now.

Alyson Tan, Age 12, Burnaby, BC
Our Lady of Mercy

I've always wondered, would my mum buy me a horse with spectacles? No, I don't think she would, would she? If she did, I'd just have to keep the poor thing. I'd ride, feed and groom and brush it just like any other horse. We'd have so much fun together! Until the unfortunate day that my friend would run away to live in the wild with her friends, without anyone to feed or clean them. There, they run wild and free. Maybe, just maybe she would bring her spectacles with her. Oh boy, would I miss that dear horse.

Emma Tarvis age 10

I've always wondered, would my mom buy me a horse with spectacles? No, I don't think she would, would she? If she did I'd just have to keep the poor thing. I'd ride, feed and groom and brush it just like any other horse. We'd have so much fun together. Until the unfortunate day that my friend would run away to live in the wild with her friends without anyone to feed or clean them. There they run wild and free. Maybe just maybe she would bring her spectacles with her. Oh boy, would I miss that dear horse.

Emma Tarvis, Age 10, Winnipeg, MB
Viscount Alexander

I've always wondered if leprechauns were real. I have never found a four leaf clover or seen the gold at the end of the rainbow. Yet, when I'm in my garden or climbing a tree sometimes it feels like someone's watching me. Sometimes it feels like the world is playing a cruel trick on me. Who knows? It could just be a leprechaun messing with my head.

Sometimes I hear noises at night. Maybe it's just a leprechaun scrummaging for food. Why is the left sock always missing? Maybe the leprechauns' feet got cold. It's always fun to wonder!

Amy Tattrie age 11

I've always wondered if leprechauns were real. I have never found a four leaf clover or seen the gold at the end of the rainbow. Yet when I'm in my garden or climbing a tree sometimes it feels like someone's watching me. Sometimes it feels like the world is playing a cruel trick on me. Who knows? It could just be a leprechaun messing with my head. Sometimes I hear noises at night. Maybe it's just a leprechaun scrummaging for food. Why is the left sock always missing? Maybe the leprechaun's feet got cold. It's always fun to wonder!

Amy Tattrie, Age 11, Truro, NS
North River Elementary

Je me suis toujours demandé pourquoi il y avait un trou sur le mur au fond de mon garde robe. Un jour je cherchais des sandales dans ma chambre. En passant j'ai trouvée une clé en dessous de mon garde robe. J'ai mis la clé dans le troue. "Grrrr." La porte s'est ouverte. Devant moi il y avait une télé, un vieux fauteil et une table avec une lettre. La lettre disait que c'était la place secrète de ma grande-mère. Là j'y vais à la place souvent pour relaxer. C'est ma découverte. Aure voir.

Kaleska Taylor, Age 12

Je me suis toujours demandé pourquoi il y avait un trou sur le mur au fond de ma garde-robe. Un jour je cherchais des sandales dans ma chambre. En passant j'ai trouvé une clé en-dessous de mon tapis. J'étais au fond de ma garde-robe. J'ai mis la clé dans le trou. « Grrrr ! » La porte s'est ouverte. Devant moi, il y avait une télé, un vieux fauteuil et une table avec une lettre. La lettre disait que c'était la place secrète de ma grand-mère. Là j'y vais à la place souvent pour relaxer. C'est ma découverte. Au revoir.

Kaleska Taylor, 12 ans, St-Jérôme, QC
Laurentien Regional H.S.

"I've always wondered if fairies were real," whispered Jennifer into Kayla's ear. The pair sat on the leafy moss-covered ground in the middle of the cool, damp wood. Dim light shone through the leaves of the tall trees. "Everything's right: honeysuckle juice, warm cream, cake, nectar…" muttered Jennifer. Kayla interjected, "Relax, we'll see them, all we have to do is…" Both girls paused and looked at each other. "Wait, watch and listen," they whispered in unison. B-eee-p! "Great, time to do homework," sighed Jennifer as her watch alarm sounded. They picked up their bikes and rode home.

Tanisha Thammavongsa 11

"I've always wondered if fairies were real," whispered Jennifer into Kayla's ear. The pair sat on the leafy moss-covered ground in the middle of the cool, damp wood. Dim light shone through the leaves of the tall tress. "Everything's right: honeysuckle juice, warm cream, cake, nectar…" muttered Jennifer. Kayla interjected, "Relax, we'll see them, all we have to do is…" Both girls paused and looked at each other. "Wait, watch and listen," they whispered in unison. B-eee-p! "Great, time to do homework," sighed Jennifer as her watch alarm sounded. They picked up their bikes and rode home.

Tanisha Thammavongsa, Age 11, Courtland, ON
South Ridge Public School

I've always wondered what it would be like to jump onto a Fairy's wings and fly to the earth's core. I could bask in the heat, not a care in the world. Dancing on the hot coals as they heat my feet. I could watch in awe what is in the middle of our curious planet, and explore the inner earth's beauty. I could lie forever just floating on my dreams and wonders over the bubbling magma. "So this is what it's like?!" I'd say to my ride, the Fairy. Then I would know what I'd always wondered!

Siobhan Theobald age 11

I've always wondered what it would be like to jump onto a fairy's wings and fly away to the earth's core. I could bask in the heat, not a care in the world. Dancing on the hot coals as they heat my feet. I could watch in awe what is in the middle of our curious planet, and explore the inner earth's beauty. I could lie forever just floating on my dreams and wonders over the bubbling magma. "So this is what it's like?!" I'd say to my ride, the fairy. Then I would know what I'd always wondered!

Siobhan Theobald, Age 11, Edmonton, AB
Our Lady of Victories

I've always wondered what it's like to be my shadow. I could scare people, play with people, and hide from people. I could do whatever I want! My shadow's name is Maria and she always hides from me. One day Maria hid for a long time and I looked all over for her, I couldn't find her anywhere! I looked in the forest and Maria sneaked up behind me and made me jump. She followed me all the way home. Then it was my turn to hide. It wasn't long before Maria found me. I am sure she was peeking!

Kailey Thurgood age:7

I've always wondered what it's like to be my shadow. I could scare people, play with people and hide from people. I could do whatever I want! My shadow's name is Maria and she always hides from me. One day Maria hid for a long time and I looked all over for her, I couldn't find her anywhere! I looked in the forest and Maria sneaked up behind me and made me jump. She followed me all the way home. Then it was my turn to hide. It wasn't long before Maria found me. I am sure she was peeking!

Kailey Thurgood, Age 7, Mississauga, ON
Millgrove Public School

I've always wondered what rainbows are made of. I think they're full of sprites and when the rainbows fade they fall to the ground, but they're so small you can't see them! They fall to their colours and work magic. Red sprites work in red fruit plants. Yellow sprites and orange sprites work together in the sand and on the sun. Pink sprites are the flower sprites. Green sprites are obviously in the trees and grass! Purple sprites help with the flowers, as well and blue sprites work in water. The world is full of sprites it's just hard to tell!

Lindsey Thurston, 11

I've always wondered what rainbows are made of. I think they're full of sprites and when the rainbows fade they fall to the ground, but they're so small you can't see them! They fall to their colours and work magic. Red sprites work in red fruit plants. Yellow sprites and orange sprites work together in the sand and on the sun. Pink sprites are the flower sprites. Green sprites are obviously in the trees and grass! Purple sprites help with the flowers, as well and blue sprites work in water. The world is full of sprites it's just hard to tell!

Lindsey Thurston, Age 11, Kingston, ON
Elginbury D.P.S.

I've always wondered why Aunt Priss ever came to visit. She always wore big, ugly pearls and a dry cleaned suit. Between three kids a dog and a monkey called Mojo the house was a zoo! Aunt Priss was dad's older sister, though he was nothing like her. There was one thing that was very odd about her. Every night we would watch her through the keyhole in the door and hear her say words like "Alakazam!" On the last day of her visit she pulled me aside and asked "Are you ready to learn my secret?"

Kacia Tolsma 11

I've always wondered why Aunt Priss ever came to visit. She always wore big, ugly pearls and a dry cleaned suit. Between three kids, a dog and a monkey called Mojo the house was a zoo! Aunt Priss was dad's older sister, though he was nothing like her. There was one thing that was very odd about her. Every night we would watch her through the keyhole in the door and hear her say words like "Alakazam!". On the last day of her visit she pulled me aside and asked "Are you ready to learn my secret?"

Kacia Tolsma, Age 11, Calgary, AB
Hillhurst Community

I've always wondered if magic is real. Everyone has heard or seen someone do a magic trick. But is it possible that some uniquely talented magicians can produce some extremely powerful spells? Since I was really little, I have always been interested in wizards, witches, and anything that had to do with Harry Potter. Now that I am a lot older, I've thought about if magic is just waving a wand and saying "Hocus Pocus". Or is magic just illusions, playing with your brain? Magic is something I have always wondered about - how it works and what it really does.

Isabella Torchia, Age 11

I've always wondered if magic is real. Everyone has heard or seen someone do a magic trick. But is it possible that some uniquely talented magicians can produce some extremely powerful spells? Since I was really little I have always been interested in wizards, witches, and anything that had to do with Harry Potter. Now that I am a lot older, I've thought about if magic is just waving a wand and saying "Hocus Pocus". Or is magic just illusions, playing with your brain? Magic is something I have always wondered about – how it works and what it really does.

Isabella Torchia, Age 11, Toronto, ON
Transfiguration of Our Lord

I've always wondered
why the moon doesn't sleep.
Autumn had came. Rustling
leaves rushed to the dark
grayish, shivery sidewalk. Woosh!
A soft wind blew across
the gigantic trees. It was
silence. I bolted outside into
the darkness. There was a
bright full moon. I've always
wondered why the moon
doesn't sleep, but I still
know wether the sun goes
down or the moon comes
up forever.

By Carmen Tran Age 9

I've always wondered why the moon doesn't sleep. Autumn had come. Rustling leaves rushed to the dark grayish, shivery sidewalk. Whoosh! A soft wind blew across the gigantic trees. It was silence. I bolted outside into the darkness. There was a bright full moon. I've always wondered why the moon doesn't sleep, but I still know whether the sun goes down or the moon comes up forever

Carmen Tran, Age 9, Calgary, AB
Patrick Airlie School

I've always wondered why the sky is blue. Did God paint it the colour of peace and humanity many years ago? I feel it shows a bit of calmness within us all. All lost hopes dwell amongst the clouds, turning the sky grey, raining hope over those in need of it. Colour re appears when all hope returns, leaving every person with calmness and hope. Wouldn't it be wonderful if every day had a blue sky, everyone is filled with hopes, dreams, and happiness. That is why I have always wondered why the sky is blue.

Chantel Trigg, 11

I've always wondered why the sky is blue. Did God paint it the colour of peace and humanity many years ago? I feel it shows a bit of calmness within us all. All lost hopes dwell amongst the clouds turning the sky grey raining hope over those in need of it. Colour re-appears in the sky when all hope returns, leaving every person with calmness and hope. Wouldn't it be wonderful if every day had a blue sky, everyone is filled with hopes, dreams, and happiness. That is why I have always wondered why the sky is blue.

Chantel Trigg, Age 11, Calgary, AB
Westmount Charter School

Je me suis toujours demandé si mon chien parlait. Ça peut paraître stupide, je sais, les chiens ne parlent pas, mais le mien est si spécial ! On dirait qu'il comprend ce que je dis ! C'est un animal si dévoué, si mignon et si compréhensif ! Quand je pleure, il vient me consoler en me faisant des câlins et en me léchant le nez. C'est un peu son langage à lui ! Il paraît qu'au Japon, ils viennent d'inventer un traducteur d'aboiements. Moi, je préfère qu'il continue à me lécher le nez !

Gabrielle Van Dongen, 12 ans

Je me suis toujours demandé si mon chien parlait. Ça peut paraître stupide, je sais, les chiens ne parlent pas, mais le mien est si spécial ! On dirait qu'il comprend ce que je dis ! C'est un animal si dévoué, si mignon et si compréhensif ! Quand je pleure, il vient me consoler en me faisant des câlins et en me léchant le nez. C'est un peu son langage à lui ! Il paraît qu'au Japon, ils viennent d'inventer un traducteur d'aboiements. Moi, je préfère qu'il continue à me lécher le nez !

Gabrielle Van Dongen, 12 ans, Montréal, QC
École Internationale

I've always wondered how street lights get turned on and off? They just turn on, but eventually turn off like magic. Is there some guy or girl in a big office flicking switches? Do they have to turn them on the same time every day? Do they go in turn them on and go home or do they go in and stay in all night? Do you know if there even is a big office? If you know anything about it, how many people work there? But then maybe there is nothing at all. Maybe the world may never know.

Jason VanWalleghem 10

I've always wondered how street lights get turned on and off?
They just turn on, but eventually turn off like magic. Is there
some guy or girl in a big office flicking switches? Do they have
to turn them on the same time every day? Do they go in turn
them on and go home or do they go in and stay in all night?
Do you know if there even is a big office? If you know
anything about it, how many people work there? But then
maybe there is nothing at all. Maybe the world may never know!

Jason VanWalleghem, Age 10, Stonewall, MB
Stonewall Centennial School

"I've always wondered why a caterpillar is so ugly when we're so beautiful," the sleek fox said to the bunny. Little did they realize that the wise old owl was listening. He hooted, "You don't know it now but soon things will be very diffrent". The fox and bunny were puzzled by this. They began to watch a caterpillar as it climbed a twig. Curiously it rolled itself into a white wrap. A few days later as they were watching the cocoon, something beautiful slowly emerged fluttering intricate wings. Then they understood to words of the wise old owl.

Victoria Veenstra   Age 11

"I've always wondered why a caterpillar is so ugly when we're so beautiful," the sleek fox said to the bunny. Little did they realize that the wise old owl was listening. He hooted, "You don't know it now but soon things will be very different." The fox and bunny were puzzled by this. They began to watch a caterpillar as it climbed a twig. Curiously it rolled itself into a white wrap. A few days later as they were watching the cocoon, something beautiful slowly emerged fluttering intricate wings. Then they understood the words of the wise old owl.

Victoria Veenstra, Age 11, Hawkestone, ON
Orillia Christian School

206

Je me suis toujours demandé pourquoi les petits frères sont si tanants ? Un jour, voulant aller magasiner avec mes amies, mon petit frère a décidé de nous accompagner. J'ai insisté pour qu'il ne vienne pas, mais c'est plus fort que lui... Une fois au centre d'achats, mes amies et moi voulions aller dans une fripperie. Mon frère lui, préfèrait le restaurant, mais je lui dit de nous suivre. Tout à coup il a disparu ! Quelques minutes plus tard le revoilà, devant moi, avec un tutu rose ! Ce qu'il peut être tanant parfois !

Amélie Veilleux, 10 ans

Je me suis toujours demandé pourquoi les petits frères sont si tannants ? Un jour, voulant aller magasiner avec mes amies, mon petit frère a décidé de nous accompagner. J'ai insisté pour qu'il ne vienne pas, mais c'est plus fort que lui… une fois au centre d'achats, mes amies et moi voulions aller dans une fripperie. Mon frère lui, préférait le restaurant, mais je lui dit de nous suivre. Tout à coup il a disparu ! Quelques minutes plus tard le revoilà, devant moi, avec un tutu rose ! Ce qu'il peut être tannant parfois !

Amélie Veilleux, 10 ans, St-Hubert, QC
École des Quatre-Vents

Je me suis toujours demandé si Tutankhamon avait eu peur avant qu'il ne soit assassiné. Quand je visitais le musée du Caire, un événement bizarre se produit. Lorsque je passais devant un vase effrité, je sentis le sol vibrer. Je ne voyais que du sable m'entourant. Je me sentis tirée vers l'avant. Un garde royal m'emmenait vers le palais où le pharaon me pardonna mes crimes et me confia sa peur de mourir. Je sentis le sol recommencer à vibrer. J'étais de retour au musée ! Après toutes ces années, j'avais la réponse à ma question !

Elizabeth Vickers-Drennan, 12 ans

Je me suis toujours demandé si Tutankhamon avait eu peur avant qu'il ne soit assassiné. Quand je visitais le musée du Caire, un événement bizarre se produit. Lorsque je passais devant un vase effrité, je sentis le sol vibrer. Je ne voyais que du sable m'entourant. Je me sentis tirée vers l'avant. Un garde royal m'emmenait vers le palais où le pharaon me pardonna mes crimes et me confia sa peur de mourir. Je sentis le sol recommencer à vibrer. J'étais de retour au musée ! Après toutes ces années, j'avais la réponse à ma question !

Elizabeth Vickers-Drennan, 12 ans, Verdun, QC
École du Mont-Bleu

I've always wondered what it would be like to be a chewy, soft, juicy piece of bubblegum that had cherry flavour to it! I'd be enjoyed by kids of all ages. They'd chew me on the swing, down the slide, reading a book, watching T.V. and even in the shower. Adults would chew me when their breath wasn't the greatest. I'd love to be loved by everyone, but what happens when my juicy, cherry flavour disappears? ... I seem to always end up "stuck"- under a desk, table or the bottom of someone's shoe! ☺

Chelsea Weir   Age-11

I've always wondered what it would be like to be a chewy, soft, juicy piece of bubble gum that had cherry flavour to it! I'd be enjoyed by kids of all ages. They'd chew me on the swing, down the slide, reading a book, watching T.V. and even in the shower. Adults would chew me when their breath wasn't the greatest. I'd love to be loved by everyone, but what happens when my juicy cherry flavour disappears? I seem to always end up "stuck" – under a desk, table to on the bottom of someone's shoe!

Chelsea Weir, Age 11, Grimsby, ON
Our Lady of Fatima

I've always wondered what happens when a chipmunk dives into his hole. Is there one room or are there many? Do they have furniture or just leaves? Are all holes connected? Do you think they have apartments or even underground cities! The holes are so narrow only one could probably fit. So, what happens when two meet? Would one have to walk backwards until he got to a room? Are baby chipmunks as mischievous as little kids are? Wouldn't it be funny if little chipmunks tried to sneak away through a side door? This is all so confusing.

Hayley * Whelan age 10

I've always wondered what happens when a chipmunk dives
into his hole. Is there one room or are there many? Do they have
furniture or just leaves? Are all holes connected? Do you think
they have apartments or even underground cities! The holes are
so narrow only one could probably fit. So, what happens when
two meet? Would one have to walk backwards until he got to a
room? Are baby chipmunks as mischievous as little kids are?
Wouldn't it be funny if little chipmunks tried to sneak away
through a side door? This is all so confusing.

Hayley Whelan, Age 10, Charlottetown, PEI
Sherwood Elementary

I've always wondered why dinosaures are extinked. Maybe they ate too much candy floss or they might have laughed so hard that they burst! They could have flew so high and flew into the sun and disapeard. Or they sat by the fire so long that they turned into ashes. They could have tryed to wash themselves so they put itself in the washer and shrunk to a tiny peace of sand. Maybe they had a pillow fight and rubed themself that they turned into a feather. Or maybe they are not extinked, they are just me and you!

THE · END

Samantha · Wong · age · eight!

I've always wondered why dinosaurs are extinct. Maybe they ate too much candy floss or they might have laughed so hard they burst! They could have flew so high and flew into the sun and disappeared. Or they sat by the fire so long that they turned into ashes. They could have tried to wash themselves so they put themselves in the washer and shrunk to a tiny piece of sand. Maybe they had a pillow fight and rubbed themselves that they turned into a feather. Or maybe they are not extinct, they are just me and you!

Samantha Wong, Age 8, Burnaby, BC
Inman Elementary School

I've always wondered why we have two eyes, and two ears but only one nose and one mouth. I know we have two ears so we can hear better and just in case one ear goes deaf. We have two eyes so we can see better and just in case one eye goes blind. But what if our nose is clogged? Shouldn't we have two noses for that? Maybe that is why we have two nostrils! Or what if we're in a rush and we're eating, shouldn't we get another mouth? That is so weird!

Alana Wong, Age 9, Mississauga, ON
Vista Heights P.S.

I've always wondered what would happen if I could go back in time, and change one thing in history. I could stop the discovery of tobacco and prevent people from suffering from cancer. If I could prevent hatred, racism, and prejudice from starting, I would have stopped the world wars from killing millions of people. But if I could only change one thing, I'd make sure Adam and Eve never ate the forbidden apple. That way we would all live in the Garden of Eden, and none of these problems would even exist.

Hilary, 12

I've always wondered what would happen if I could go back in time, and change one thing in history. I could stop the discovery of tobacco and prevent people from suffering from cancer. If I could prevent hatred, racism, and prejudice from starting, I would have stopped the world wars from killing millions of people. But if I could only change one thing, I'd make sure Adam and Eve never ate the forbidden apple. That way we would all live in the Garden of Eden, and none of these problems would even exist.

Hilary Zarnett, Age 12, Toronto, ON
United Synagogue Day School

I've always wondered why the ocean is so big and beautiful. Every night I walk along the silent shore and stare at the last of the blazing sun, the night sky a pink marvel as the sun sets. The ocean is calm and quiet. The animals are fast asleep waiting for the shimmering sun to shine upon the entire ocean, with one blast of sunlight. The moon awakens to see everyone fast asleep. His reflection soothes the sea, like a night light for many of the creatures. Now I know why the sea is so beautiful and magical because of Mother Nature.

Alana Zelter age 11.

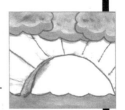

I've always wondered why the ocean is so big and beautiful. Every night I walk along the silent shore and stare at the last of the blazing sun, the night sky a pink marvel as the sun sets. The ocean is calm and quiet. The animals are fast asleep waiting for the shimmering sun to shine upon the entire ocean, with one blast of sunlight. The moon awakens to see everyone fast asleep. His reflection soothes the sea, like a night light for many of the creatures. Now I know why the sea is so beautiful and magical because of Mother Nature.

Alana Zelter, Age 11, Vancouver, BC
Brooke Elementary

Illustrated by/Illustration par Tiziana Guido

I've always wondered how it would feel to be a super hero!
I would be Super-Sam. I would be tall and friendly. I would
surely have the eyes of a lynx to see those in distress. I would
also have attentive ears to hear the cries and the crying of
people in pain. My hands would be big enough to pick up those
who have fallen. And my heart as big as the moon to love the
unfortunate ones. Come to think about it,
if I act as a good samaritan each day,
I am already a super hero!

ENGLISH TRANSLATION
OF FIRST PLACE STORY

Samuel Turcotte, 10 ans, St-Hyacinthe, QC
École Douville